PHOTOCOPIABLES

YEAR

Paul and Jean Noble

CREDITS

Authors
Paul and Jean Noble

Editor
Dulcie Booth

Assistant Editor
Sally Gray

Series designer
Lynne Joesbury

Designers
Paul Cheshire and Rachel Warner

Illustrations
Gaynor Berry

Cover photographs
Manipulated images © Photodisc (globe, dice, magnet, paintbrush, disk);
© Digital Vision (hand); © Stockbyte (mask)

Published by Scholastic Ltd,
Villiers House,
Clarendon Avenue,
Leamington Spa,
Warwickshire
CV32 5PR
Printed by Bell & Bain Ltd, Glasgow
Text © Paul and Jean Noble
© 2002 Scholastic Ltd
4 5 6 7 8 9 0   5 6 7 8 9 0 1

Visit our website at www.scholastic.co.uk

British Library Cataloguing-in-Publication Data
A catalogue record for this book is available from
the British Library.

ISBN 0-439-01988-5

CONTENTS

INTRODUCTION

Teaching Year 1

In Year 1 the National Curriculum begins in earnest when children are introduced to the whole range of subjects that it prescribes. For some teachers this structuring of both subject matter and teaching methodology, defined with increasing detail and precision, is a godsend, releasing them from burdens of curriculum construction so that they can concentrate on the children and the teaching process. But even those who feel this as a growing pressure of constraint rather than an easing of the pressure of responsibility know that Year 1 is a year of special freedom. Children are not at the beginning or the end of any stage of education or schooling, they are usually, by this time, well-socialised into the norms of behaviour in a school community. They also face a year unsullied by any standard prescribed tests – the year is SAT free.

That is not to say that teaching Year 1 is easy; teaching is rarely that. The range and coverage of the curriculum is daunting enough in itself, and you can never be entirely free from the notion that Year 1 is the year that prepares children for the important SAT year to come. Nevertheless, it is a particularly enjoyable year to teach, as there is an eagerness to learn coupled, very often, with a cheerful, bright-eyed, bushy-tailed innocence that helps to offset the sweat and toil involved.

This book is intended to ease some of this toil and mop up some of the sweat. It draws on substantial teaching experience and provides an accessible, easy-to-use support for teachers under pressure in the classroom. You will find this book particularly helpful when you are under pressure of time or you have to meet the needs of voracious learners. Supply teachers and others 'caught on the hop' will also be able to rely on this material to help them cope with demanding days. But remember, the photocopiable sheets are intended to support your teaching, not to do it for you. A whole school full of over-heated photocopiers will not make children learn. It is for you to capture their interest and stimulate and provide for the mental and physical activities that are a prerequisite to accompany learning at this stage.

What the photocopiable sheets cover

This book is based upon the range of curriculum subjects and experiences that are described within *The National Curriculum: Handbook for primary teachers in England* (www.nc.uk.net). Inevitably, weighting has been given to the core subjects (English, mathematics and science) and the worksheets have been compiled bearing in mind the demands of the

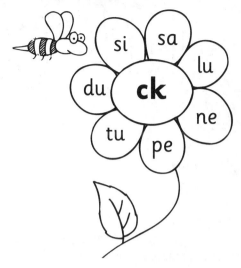

Literacy and Numeracy Strategies, as well as QCA subject guidance. The non-core foundation subjects (design and technology, information and communication technology, history, geography, art and design and music), except PE, are included but in varying degrees, depending upon the suitability of the content to the photocopiable format. Non-foundation subjects such as religious education and PSHE and citizenship are also covered. The photocopiable sheets do not, of course, cover everything and they cannot constitute a complete curriculum – giving a very young child a photocopiable sheet for PE would not make much sense – but they do aim to give essential support for the core of your teaching. Rather like basic car insurance, the cover provided here is fundamental rather than comprehensive. Nobody would want Year 1 children to overdose on photocopiable sheets.

The choice of photocopiable sheets was made on the following grounds:

● Content and activities must translate sensibly onto the photocopiable format. (Activities that are predominantly 'hands-on', colour dependent, or oral have been largely avoided.)

● Activities must be worthwhile (in that they contribute towards achieving specific learning objectives) and interesting for the children.

● Subject matter should relate directly to the prescribed National Curriculum.

● Content should satisfy the demands of the Numeracy and Literacy Strategies where possible.

Children of this age require teaching that includes a great deal of practice and repetition, but we have largely avoided providing repetitious sheets in favour of range of cover and in order to keep the book to a manageable size. However, suggestions for reinforcement and extension are included in the teachers' notes.

Using the material

Before using one of the photocopiable sheets it is recommended that you read the teachers' notes that accompany it. These have been deliberately kept brief and contain four sections:

Objective

This states the teaching objective (s). Every objective is linked to the curriculum guidance issued by the government – in numeracy and literacy, for example, the objectives match targets specified in the Numeracy and Literacy Strategies. Objectives have been stated in direct and non-pretentious terms. However, it is not claimed that children completing a particular sheet will therefore fully achieve that objective – we wish that teaching and learning were that easy.

What to do

This section provides notes on how the activity should be introduced and worked through with the children. These instructions repeatedly refer to the adult support that children will require and to the importance of talk and discussion. It is very important to get Year 1 children to 'think out loud' as an aid to learning. We have also made the assumption that Year 1 children will not, by and large, have reached a high level of reading competence, and we expect that they will be given oral instruction and support. Instructions, when given on the sheets, are therefore kept as brief as possible and sometimes they will serve as a memory jogger to the teacher rather than instructions to the child. The teachers' notes state when, and what, equipment will be required (usually very little), how the activity might be taught (whole class, group or individual instruction), and the degree of teacher support that is likely to be needed.

Differentiation

This section covers many strategies for differentiation, some of which are very simple. Often, all that is needed to give all the children in a group access to a particular activity is a change in the extent of the attention and instruction given. More able children will be able to proceed with the minimum of instruction; less able children may need adult support throughout an activity. It is rarely the case that an entirely different activity will be needed to differentiate in order for an objective to be achieved, but where appropriate you will find suggestions in the teachers' notes.

Extension

This section suggests follow-up and extension activities. Extension activities can be used as a form of differentiation for more able children but they are mainly intended to provide some form of reinforcement to help achieve the objective. Apart from where particular apparatus or teaching is required, most of the extension activities could be completed at home. It is recommended that the issues being dealt with (including the support provided for parents), the value of completing the work at home and competing demands on the children all be considered before homework is set. Teachers seeking further extension work, or more differentiation for able children, should consult subsequent books in this series.

Progression

The order of the photocopiable sheets has been kept as logical as possible – the activity on sheet one would usually be expected to be taught before sheet ten, for example. However, this order will not necessarily match the order of your teaching programme, and in some subject areas there is simply no obvious order for the teaching of particular activities. Nevertheless, a thread of progression runs through the book, and, more visibly, through the series. This is inevitable as the material is tied to a progressive National Curriculum. It does mean, however, that reference can be made, both forward and back, for more or less challenging activities for the children to undertake.

ENGLISH

The main thrust of these photocopiable sheets has been determined by the National Literacy Strategy, so you will find that the material matches the termly programme for Year 1 set down within it. Coverage is selective. This is not only for reasons of space, or because there are whole areas of learning literacy that are not best tackled using photocopiables (such as role-play) but because it is not necessary to teach every aspect of English in detail. For example, not every consonant cluster needs detailed treatment. Nevertheless, the following sheets range across all aspects of the Literacy Strategy with emphasis on word- and text-level work, material that lends itself more readily to the worksheet format.

In this chapter you will find useful reinforcement work on phonological awareness, phonics and spelling. There are also sheets on word recognition, graphic knowledge and spelling, and some on vocabulary extension. Handwriting has largely been left alone. Where possible use has been made of the high frequency word list given in the appendix to the Strategy. Grammatical awareness, sentence construction and punctuation are covered too, but you will find that there are no barriers between the various headings. Children might be constructing sentences in ways that involve reading, word recognition and rhymes as well as punctuation. It is not always possible, or desirable, to separate the building bricks of language from the mortar that binds them together.

For further details of the teaching programme, apart from *The National Curriculum* and *The National Literacy Strategy* itself, you should consult other relevant government publications, in particular those published by the Standards and Effectiveness Unit. Although the range of some of the publications can be off-putting where it encompasses more than one key stage, they do contain useful material within them. See, for example, *The NLS Word Level Work, Activity Resource Bank, Module 2*, published jointly by DfEE and OUP.

Rhyme and count (page 13)

Objective: To develop phonological awareness by practising the ability to rhyme.

What to do: The children should already be familiar with this and other similar rhymes. The real value of this exercise lies in the oral work that accompanies it. Recite each part of the rhyme with a group inviting them to complete the missing rhyme each time. Then challenge the children to cut out and reassemble the rhyme in the correct order using number knowledge and rhyme to help them. They could then stick the strips onto a new sheet of paper and illustrate them.

Differentiation: The sheet itself is best completed before it is cut out – the picture clues will act as an *aide memoire* – although you may prefer to cut the sections out first, depending on the ability of the children. Where writing poses difficulties for children, you can differentiate by letting these children cut out the picture words and stick these into the blank rhymes. Less able children might also work in pairs or small groups to tackle this sheet.

Extension: Recite and learn other rhymes (number rhymes are common). Make up (out loud) variations on a known rhyme, such as this, so that they practise hearing the sounds. Sense and spelling are not important, rather the sounds themselves.

Nobody spoke (page 14)

Objectives: To practise the ability to rhyme and to generate rhyming strings.

What to do: This photocopiable sheet focuses on listening. Read the complete rhymes to the children before they attempt to do the sheet. The rhyme is based upon an old Oxfordshire nursery rhyme but you could adapt it to fit your local area.

Differentiation: You may need to reinforce the notion of similar sounds with some children. Play oral games, for example make up new verses such as *Batley and Brill were silent and still; Jack and Jill were silent and still; Wendy and Bill were silent and still; Over the hill they were silent and still*; and so on.

Extension: Get the children to generate rhymes using the wheels given at the bottom of the sheet. Less able children need not write them down but encourage the more able children to do so and to go beyond the examples given. Can they generate any more rhymes?

Rhyme lines (page 15)

Objective: To sort CVC words into rhyming sets.

What to do: Read the words on the T-shirts out loud with the children first. The children should then complete the rhyming strings by writing the words from the T-shirts at the bottom of the sheet onto a T-shirt on the correct washing line. Children may well do this by sight so when they have completed the sheet, they should recite the strings to an adult to check that they have recognised the rhyming set.

Differentiation: The exercise itself is an oral challenge but some children may find the writing part difficult. Less able children could sort the words simply by using a pencil line to link the correct T-shirt to the correct washing line. Alternatively, an adult could cut out the words from the bottom of the page for the child to stick onto the correct line.

Extension: Hang out more washing! The sound is important not the sense. Create another washing line or lines with rhyming strings of CVC words but put in a misfit. Can the children spot which one it is? This could be a homework activity.

Lewis' ladder game (page 16)

Objectives: To begin to secure the ability to hear initial and final phonemes in CVC words and to be able to segment all three phonemes.

What to do: The invention of this game is usually credited to Lewis Carroll, hence Lewis' ladder. You can get from any CVC word to any other CVC word in three steps as is shown here, so you can easily demonstrate the idea using other examples before the children attempt this sheet. Ensure you direct the children to use the picture clues or they may come up with perfectly valid answers but not the ones given here. The answers to the sheet are: dog, cog, cot, cat; and pin, pan, pat, hat.

Differentiation: Provide the initial phoneme in the changed word as a prop to less able children. Alternatively, if you have adult support, give the children oral clues to help them name the object drawn.

Extension: This is a splendid game once the children have grasped the principle. Get them to invent ladders of their own. Draw ladders and clues for others to fathom. An ideal puzzle for homework.

On TV – cut and stick (page 17)

Objective: To read on sight some high frequency words from the high frequency word list.

What to do: Although this is basically a cut-and-stick photocopiable, the children can copy the words into the correct blank arrows to avoid the delicate and sometimes messy process of sticking. Make sure that the children notice the directions of the arrows as this is a key clue to placement.

Differentiation: Some less able children may cope perfectly well with the sticking process, however let those struggling connect the words and blanks using a pencil line. Talk to less able children about the picture in detail if they are finding the activity difficult. More able children can fill in the blank arrow with another word based on the picture, not already used.

Extension: Children might take these words home to learn. Make labels for other words on the high frequency list – display them, play games with them, get the children to recognise and memorise them. They are not all nouns, of course.

Months of the year (page 18)

Objective: To practise sight recognition of the words for the months of the year (included on the high frequency list).

What to do: Any activity that helps the children to become familiar with the words used for the months of the year is valuable – there should be charts on the wall, dates on the blackboard, birthday charts and so on. The children need to know the words before they can be expected to learn the order. Read the poem to the children perhaps several times over a period of days. They can then fill in the months of the year on the sheet. (NB: A gilly-flower is a clove-scented pink wallflower – *Dianthus carophyllus*.)

Differentiation: Although some children may not find the ordering of the months difficult in itself, the poem is not easy. You could limit the problem by dealing with a few verses at a time. Make sure a list of the months is displayed where all children can see.

Extension: Give the children cards with the first six months written on them. Ask them to place them in order and to draw a picture illustrating something that reminds them of one of the months (for example, a birthday, the weather, a holiday and so on). They may need help with this. Perhaps they could do this at home with parental help.

Word factory (page 19)

Objective: To investigate, read and spell words with final consonant clusters -ff, -ll, -ss.

What to do: Encourage experimentation on this photocopiable sheet. First make sure that the children know what sounds are made by the final consonant clusters. The first machine throws out beginnings of  words, the second – endings. Do they fit to make a real word? When the children have finished they should sound out the words to an adult.

Differentiation: A classroom assistant on hand to sound out the words with the children is obviously a bonus. Some children may find joining the letters difficult and will find it easier to try out new words using cards. Make cards with beginnings and endings on them, using different-coloured card for the three sorts of letter clusters.

Extension: Get the children to find more words that end in these double consonant clusters. Make a list of them at home.

Spelling bee (page 20)

Objective: To investigate, read and spell words ending in -*ck* and -*ng*.

What to do: Explain to the children how a bee buzzes around, landing on petals before it goes to the centre of the flower to gather nectar. They should make words by putting together the petal beginning and the centre ending, then write them on the lines provided. Note that all combinations make sense.

Differentiation: The children will find it helpful to sound out the words. Some children may need adult support.

Extension: Children could generate other words with these endings as a homework task. All the combinations here work, but others may not, for example *cick*. Be aware that, left to their own devices, children may by chance or otherwise, produce a number of words that you would not wish them to use.

Word slide (page 21)

Objective: To discriminate, read and spell words with initial consonant clusters.

What to do: You might want to make and mount the word slides on card for the children. It comes in two parts but the beginnings and endings should be clear to the children – as the only way that you can make words without overlapping the cards is by having the two sections in the correct order. Show the children how the strips can slide together to produce words. Point out that they are not all valid words. The children should write down, on a new piece of paper, as many combinations as they can that are genuine words.

Differentiation: Check before they start that the children can make the required sounds. Children who find it difficult to sound the consonant clusters should only attempt the activity with adult support. They can still generate words for an adult to sound but then must identify the genuine words themselves.

Extension: There are many consonant cluster blends (see appendix list 3 in the Literacy Strategy) and you could make other similar word slides or challenge children to make their own. In the latter case you must limit the number of blends.

Beginnings (page 22)

Objective: To discriminate, read and spell words with initial consonant clusters.

What to do: This is another way of tackling the teaching of consonant blends. A choice of four consonant blends

is given at the top of the sheet and the children have to sound out and complete the unfinished words by filling in the blanks with the correct blend. They use the picture clues to help them to do so.

Differentiation: Even where children are working unaided, get them to sound out the words as they make them. Less able children may need adult support in doing this.

Extension: Ask the children to make some picture word collections similar to those on the sheet. The more able children could simply collect words that fit – illustrating tends to limit the choice of words to objects they can draw.

Finish the job (1) (page 23)

Objective: To discriminate, read and spell words with final consonant clusters.

What to do: This is simply an endings variation of the previous sheet. Encourage the children to approach it in a similar way, filling in the blanks with the correct consonant blend given at the top of the page.

Differentiation/extension: These will be the same as 'Beginnings', see above.

Finish the job (2) (page 24)

Objective: To discriminate, read and spell words with final consonant clusters.

What to do: See the notes for 'Beginnings' and 'Finish the job (1)' above.

Differentiation/extension: These will be the same as 'Beginnings' and 'Finish the job (1)', see above.

Say and spell: 'ea' in seat (page 25)

Objective: To discriminate, read and spell common spelling patterns for the long vowel phoneme *ea*.

What to do: First the children must recognise and be able to sound out the long vowel sound *ea* in the word *seat*. Demonstrate to the children how to follow the first word, joining the *s* and the *t* to the long vowel sound to make the word *seat* as written in the box. The children should then assemble the rest of the words on the photocopiable sheet by first sounding out the word then writing it.

Differentiation: As this is based on oral work and the ability to be able to hear and say the sounds represented, less able children will need oral support in the first instance. They might seek out similar words in their reading books and in other books and on displays around the classroom.

Extension: Give the children the last part of the sheet as a homework challenge. Making further words really requires the ability to read and form more complex words such as *wh-ea-t*, *squ-ea-k* and so on. However, more words can be generated simply by extending the ones given for example, *heat-ing*, *neat-ly*.

Say and spell: 'ee' in weep

(page 26)

Objective: To discriminate, read and spell common spelling patterns for the long vowel phoneme *ee*.
What to do: This is a variation on the previous activity 'Say and spell – 'ea' in seat'. See the notes above.
Differentiation/extension: See above.

Say and spell: 'ai' in paid (page 27)

Objective: To discriminate, read and spell common spelling patterns for the long vowel phoneme *ai*.
What to do: This is a variation on the previous activity 'Say and spell – 'ea' in seat'. See the notes above.
Differentiation/extension: See above.

Say and spell: 'igh' in light

(page 28)

Objective: To discriminate, read and spell common spelling patterns for the long vowel phoneme *ie* (spelled *igh*).
What to do: This is a variation on the previous activity 'Say and spell – 'ea' in seat'. See the notes above.
Differentiation/extension: See above.

Say and spell: 'oa' in boat (page 29)

Objective: To discriminate, read and spell common spelling patterns for the long vowel phoneme *oa*.
What to do: This is a variation on the previous activity 'Say and spell – 'ea' in seat'. See the notes above.
Differentiation/extension: See above.

Say and spell: 'oo' in hoot

(page 30)

Objective: To discriminate, read and spell common spelling patterns for the long vowel phoneme *oo*.
What to do: This is a variation on the previous activity 'Say and spell – ea in seat'. See the notes above.
Differentiation/extension: See above.

Sentence singers (page 31)

Objective: To learn to expect reading to make sense and to be aware of the grammar of a sentence.
What to do: In this activity the children should say (or sing, if you want the noise!) the words being uttered by the people and animals illustrated. Each utterance has a capital letter and a full stop but doesn't necessarily make sense as a sentence. Which songs are sensible sentences? Get the children to lightly colour in the sentences that make sense, leaving the nonsense ones alone.
Differentiation: If some children cannot read the utterances then an adult on hand to help will solve the problem. However, children do need to have reached some understanding of what makes sense and what does not. In this instance giving lots of examples of incomplete and muddled phrases that make no sense is an enjoyable worthwhile exercise. Children will usually find it funny, give them an example such as *Not you is*. Ask them: *Would you ever say this? Does it make sense?*
Extension: Making nonsense or making sense? Ask the children to generate more examples of their own – they may have fun illustrating them. You could ask for three sentences that make sense and one phrase that doesn't. Emphasis should be on the correct not the incorrect!

Dream sentences (page 32)

Objective: To learn to expect reading to make sense and to be aware of the grammar of a sentence.
What to do: This is similar to the activity above, 'Sentence singers'. Ask the children: *Who is dreaming in proper sentences?* Again, get the children to colour in the sentences that make sense.
Differentiation/extension: See 'Sentence singers' above. Can they make the utterances that don't make sense into proper sentences? For example, *Sheep and cows are farm animals*.

Build brick sentences (page 33)

Objectives: To learn to expect reading to make sense and to be aware of the grammar of a sentence. To investigate words that fit to make sense.
What to do: Approach this cautiously – there are pitfalls for the unwary. Colour in one brick in the first pile, then in the second and so on, to create a sentence. The bricks do not have to be in a line as long as there is one from each pile only. Show the children how to create one sentence as an example and challenge them to make five or six sentences. The catch is that it is possible to make more but only by using a brick more than once. This is fine for the more able children to tackle but can become a colour muddle that you will find hard to disentangle.
Differentiation: Less able children will make fewer sentences but quantity is not the object – sense is. Give support with the reading where appropriate. Once the children grasp the principle, they will enjoy trying to make more than six sentences. It is possible to make six without double usage.

Extension: Asking the children to write the sentences down instead of colouring them in avoids muddle and allows bricks to be used in more than one sentence. You could follow up by playing this as a class game, generating lots of 'sentences' and spotting those that make no sense.

Say and write: same sounds

(page 34)

Objective: To learn common spelling patterns for each of the long vowel phonemes, in this case *a–e; i–e; o–e; u–e*.

What to do: Explain the examples given in the left-hand column to the children, sounding the words out loud. The children then work across the page from left to right. Each row contains the same long vowel phoneme. By imitation and deduction, the children should be able to complete the rest of the row. The picture clues will help.

Differentiation/extension: This is a similar exercise to the one in 'Say and spell: 'ea' in seat' and similar sheets but is slightly more difficult because of the split letters. See the notes for 'Say and spell: 'ea' in seat'.

Capital beginnings (page 35)

Objective: To use capital letters for the beginning of a sentence.

What to do: Show the children how they must select the capital letter from the letter stands on the left to fit into the blank and make the sentence complete.

Differentiation: Give less able children no choice – delete the left column and provide instead the capital letters required. They then simply select the correct one. You might also need to read the sentences to the children before they start the activity.

Extension: Give the children more examples to complete. Provide sentences with the first letter written in lower case. The children have to spot what is wrong and provide the capital letter needed.

Capital titles (page 36)

Objective: To read and write place names and personal names and titles using capital letters correctly.

What to do: Point out to the children that the labels and titles provided on the photocopiable sheet have lower case letter beginnings where capitals should be. Their task is to fill in the blanks to make the titles correct. As the sheet includes place names that the children may not be familiar with, an adult should read these for them. The place names could also be the focus of a class discussion: *Has anyone been to London?* and so on.

Differentiation: Less able children may find reading the words difficult and will need an adult to help them.

Extension: Reinforce the lesson with lots of examples of place names and people's names. For homework, ask the children to write the name of their street, town or village, and county using capital letters correctly. Alternatively, they could make a list of all the names and titles of all the teachers in the school.

Missing titles (page 37)

Objective: To read and write book titles using capital letters correctly.

What to do: Read and discuss the six book titles on the photocopiable sheet with the children. Do they recognise any? Here is an opportunity to talk about and show the children the titles of books, where and how they are written, the spine and so on. You might read one of the books listed (*Mr Tick the Teacher*, for example). Show the children how capital letters are usually used for titles. Show examples. The children should then copy the titles onto the spines correctly using capital letters to replace the lower case ones provided.

Differentiation: Add examples of the capital letters required to the sheet so that less able children can select the appropriate ones.

Extension: Follow-up should be along the lines suggested in the notes for the previous sheet. Children could copy the titles of three of their favourite books at home.

Hands up! (page 38)

Objective: To learn to add question marks to questions.

What to do: This class is clearly trouble, they are full of questions – or are they? Read them out to the class. A question demands an answer. Are there any statements on the sheet that do not? Explain to the children that when we ask a question, we need to add a question mark to the end of the sentence. Get them to add question marks to the sentences in the speech bubbles that are questions. To reinforce this learning, get the children to write the questions out for themselves afterwards.

Differentiation: Play a game with a group of less able children. Keep asking them questions interspersed with statements. When they spot a question they should draw the shape of a question mark in the air. Give them copy practice at making the squiggle used. Get them to colour in the questions (only) in the speech bubbles before they add the question marks to check that they have understood.

Extension: Ask children to search a book to find three questions. Copy them. This could be a homework task.

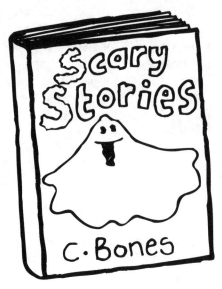

Differentiation: You may need to give some children more clues to put them on the right track. What do sentences begin with? Talk the children through each example. Does 'my boots ate Fido' make sense? If writing out the sentences poses a difficulty for less able children, try enlarging the sheet and cutting out the words in each sentence so that they need only reorder them. Stick these words on separate cards to ease handling.

Extension: Ask the children to write a sentence and to reorder the words in such a way that they create a nonsense sentence for their friend to unravel.

Story sense (page 39)

Objectives: To identify basic elements in a story such as beginning, middle, ending, and to use this knowledge to retell a story in the correct order.

What to do: Cut up this photocopiable before the children use it. Lay out the sentences on the desk and explain to the children that they must place the sentences in the correct order (or an acceptable variation). Muddle them up and try again. Ideally this should be done in small groups that must agree on the order.

Differentiation: Help less able children by suggesting a strategy. How do they think the story ended? How did it begin? Which sentence fits at the end and which at the beginning? Can they say what would happen next? Make sure that the children read and understand the sentences. You may want to read out the sentences first to the children.

Extension: Challenge the children to add an extra sentence to this story. Make sure they place it where it makes sense. More able children might add several sentences and illustrate them. They could complete this at home.

Rick Wrong and Rose Right
(page 40)

Objective: To apply reading skills and use contextual and other clues to order sentences correctly.

What to do: Explain the example given on the sheet to the children. Note that the words are muddled and no additional words are needed, just rearrangement. Stress that Rick is always wrong and Rose is always right. Show the children that Rick is wrong by reading all the 'sentences' that he has written incorrectly. Can they write what Rose Right would write? Challenge them to make sense from the silly lines written.

Bookshelf (page 41)

Objective: To use contextual and visual clues to predict the content of a book.

What to do: The aim is to draw a line from the object or person on the right to the book from which they are *most* likely to have come.

Differentiation: Reading the titles of the books, identifying the objects, and observing the clues given on the book's cover, are all prerequisites to being able to complete this task. Where children fall down in any of these, they will need adult help to tease out the meanings. Point at the objects. Can they name them? Point at the books. What are they about? And so on. Get the children to draw a line connecting the objects to the books.

If you have *story bags* let children play with these. Give them two different bags and ask them to sort the correct objects into the correct bags to fit the book in the bag. This exercise is essentially a two-dimensional version of the story bag. (Story bags are collections of objects, soft toys and so on that are placed together with a story book in a bag. They encourage reading and help to make a story come alive for small children. They can be 'home-made' very successfully with a little imagination and DIY skills.)

Extension: Get the children to create their own examples. There is room on the sheet for them to draw a similar example of their own, although some might rise to the challenge of bringing a book to school with an artefact that might fit within it. Give the children examples of what you mean and what you do not mean (or cannot cope with) or you may find that some keen child will bring a book about horses and their pet pony to school, or a book on fishing and the remains of yesterday's fish supper!

Rhyme and count

Complete the rhymes. Then cut them out and put them in the right order.

✂

One, two,
Buckle my _____.

Nine, ten,
A big fat _____.

Five, six,
Pick up _____.

Three, four,
Knock at the _____.

Seven, eight,
Lay them _____.

✂

| door | shoe | hen | sticks | straight |

Nobody spoke

● Fill in the rhymes with the words from the right.

I went to Noke

But nobody _____.

I went to Slad

It was just as _____.

Batley and Brill

Were silent and _____.

But I went to Tring

And they started to _____.

still

sing

spoke

bad

● Use the letters to make some new rhymes.

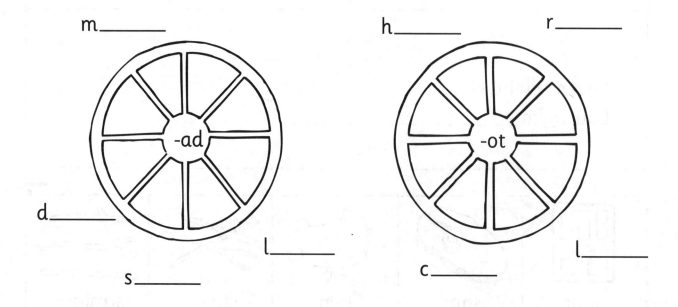

m_____

d_____

s_____

-ad

l_____

h_____

c_____

r_____

-ot

l_____

Rhyme lines

Hang the shirts from the basket on the right line.

■SCHOLASTIC

Lewis' ladder game

Change **one** letter at a time. Can you make **dog** into **cat**?

dog

cat

pin

On TV – cut and stick

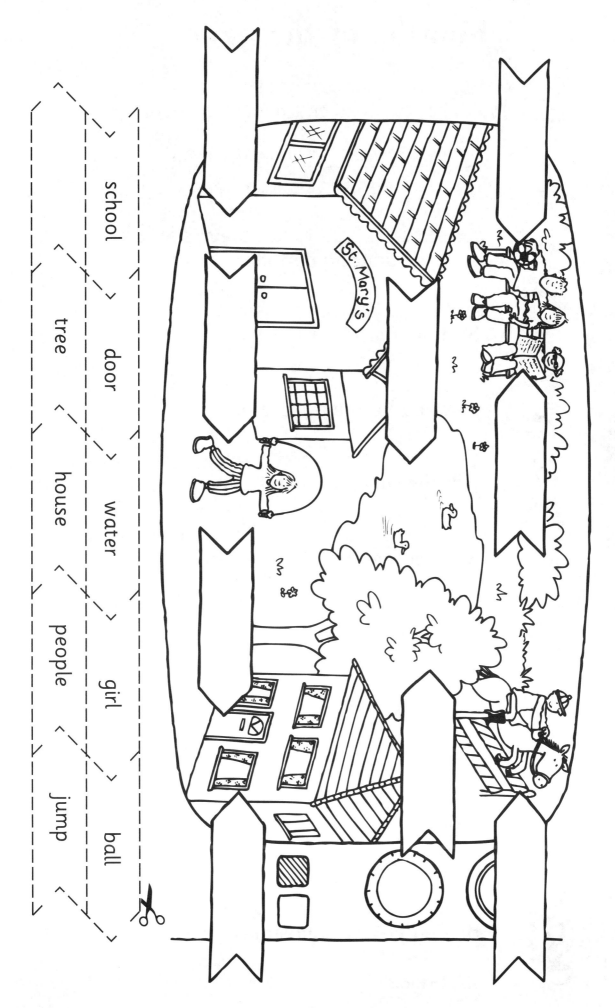

school

door

tree

water

house

people

girl

jump

ball

Months of the year

_____ brings the snow;
Makes the toes and fingers glow.

_____ brings the rain,
Thaws the frozen ponds again.

_____ brings breezes loud and shrill,
Stirs the dancing daffodil.

_____ brings the primrose sweet,
Scatters daisies at our feet.

_____ brings flocks of pretty lambs,
Skipping by their fleecy dams.

_____ brings tulips, lilies, roses;
Fills the children's hands with posies.

Hot _____ brings cooling showers,
Strawberries and gilly-flowers.

_____ brings the sheaves of corn,
Then the Harvest home is borne.

Warm _____ brings the fruit,
Sportsmen then begin to shoot.

Fresh _____ brings the pheasant;
Then to gather nuts is pleasant.

Dull _____ brings the blast,
Then the leaves are falling fast.

Chill _____ brings the sleet,
Blazing fire and Christmas treat.

Sara Coleridge

Word factory

Put together beginnings and endings. How many words can you make? Write them in the box below.

Spelling bee

Use the endings in the centre of the flowers to make as many words as you can.

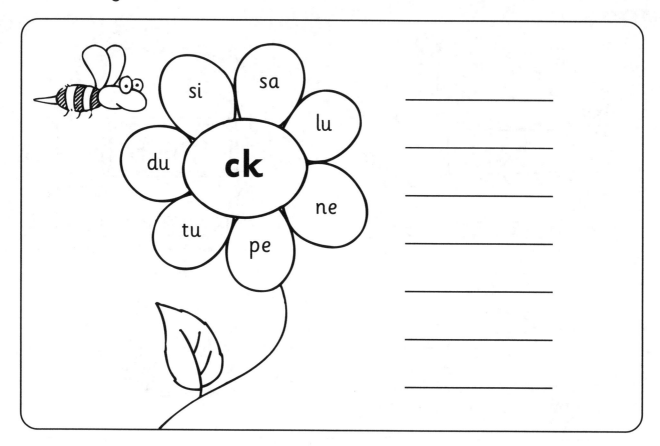

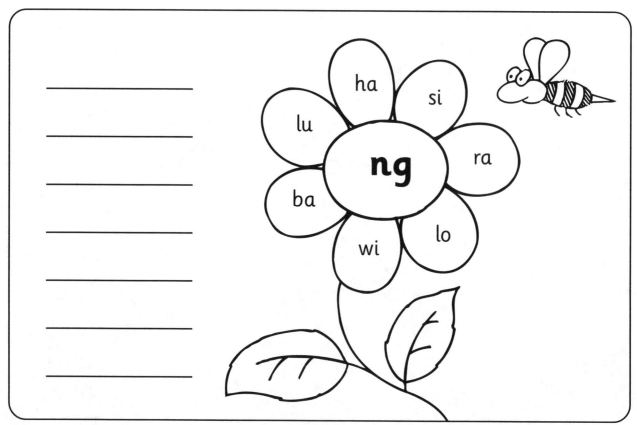

Word slide

Cut out the two strips. Slide the two strips to make as many words as you can.

br	
bl	
cl	
cr	an
dr	ow
gl	aw
gr	ate
pl	ip
sk	ot
st	ick
tr	ill

Beginnings

Use these beginnings to finish the words. fl fr sn spr

_____y	_____og	_____ail	_____ing
_____ay	_____ow	_____ead	_____ake
_____ag	_____uit	_____ill	_____ame
_____out	_____an	_____eeze	_____ute

Finish the job (1)

Use these endings to finish the words.   ld   nd   lk   nk

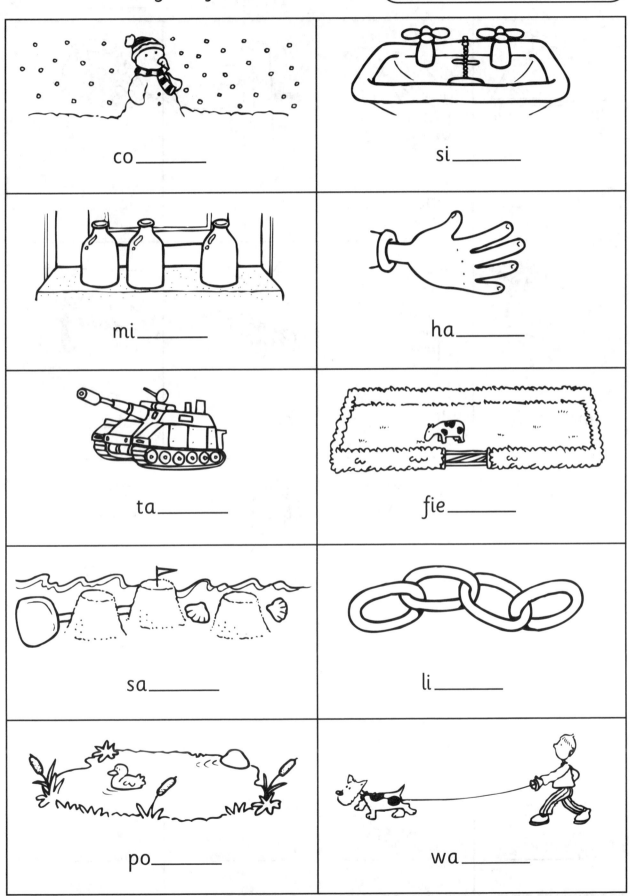

co _____

si _____

mi _____

ha _____

ta _____

fie _____

sa _____

li _____

po _____

wa _____

Finish the job (2)

Use these endings to finish the words.   (st   nch   mp   sk)

de_____	bu_____	po_____	la_____
ma_____	li_____	bra_____	sta_____
li_____	coa_____	mi_____	lu_____
ca_____	fla_____	tu_____	pu_____

Say and spell: 'ea' in seat

- Say and spell the words below.

s	e a	t

seat

n	e a	t

h	e a	t

b	e a	t

l	e a	p

m	e a	t

- Can you make any more 'ea' words?

Say and spell: 'ee' in weep

● Say and spell the words below.

w e e p → weep

d e e p →

k e e p →

f e e l →

s e e d →

m e e t →

● Can you make any more 'ee' words?

Say and spell: 'ai' in paid

● Say and spell the words below.

p   a i   d   p<u>ai</u>d

r   a i   d

w   a i   t

tr   a i   n

st   a i   n

l   a i   d

● Can you make any more 'ai' words?

Say and spell: 'igh' in light

● Say and spell the words below.

l — igh — t [light]

t — igh — t [ ]

s — igh — [ ]

br — igh — t [ ]

h — igh — [ ]

f — igh — t [ ]

● Can you make any more 'igh' words?

[ ]

Say and spell: 'oa' in boat

- Say and spell the words below.

b	oa	t	boat
c	oa	t	
l	oa	d	
t	oa	d	
s	oa	p	
r	oa	d	

- Can you make any more 'oa' words?

Say and spell: 'oo' in hoot

- Say and spell the words below.

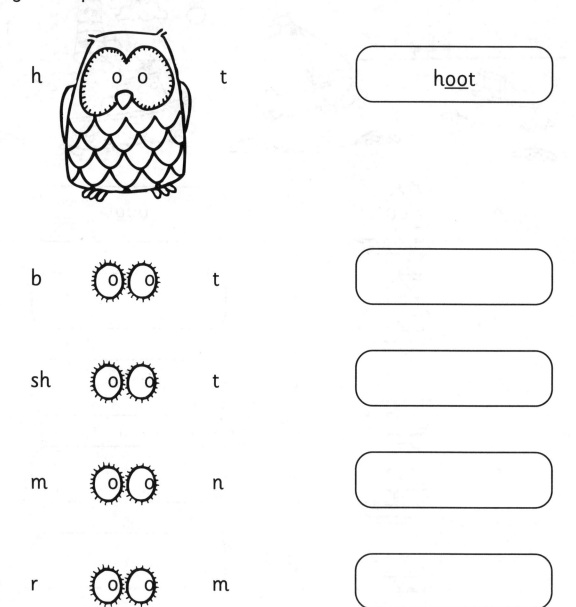

h   o o   t

h<u>oo</u>t

b   o o   t

sh   o o   t

m   o o   n

r   o o   m

- Can you make any more 'oo' words?

Sentence singers

Colour in the sentences that make sense.

I am a tall man.

My song is.

Bow and wow.

Polly is the name of my dolly.

This is a hot bath.

Dream sentences

Colour in the sentences that make sense.

I like my bike.

Sheep and cows are.

Chips and peas.

Miss Jones is my favourite teacher.

I want a bone.

Mouse, mouse, mouse.

Build brick sentences

Colour a brick in each pile to make a sentence.

Sarah	ran	to	my	table.
I	fell	for	a	mum.
They	ate	by	his	bed.
Dan	jumped	down	the	shop.
He	slept	on	her	box.
She	sang	over	their	stairs.

Say and write: same sounds

Complete the words.

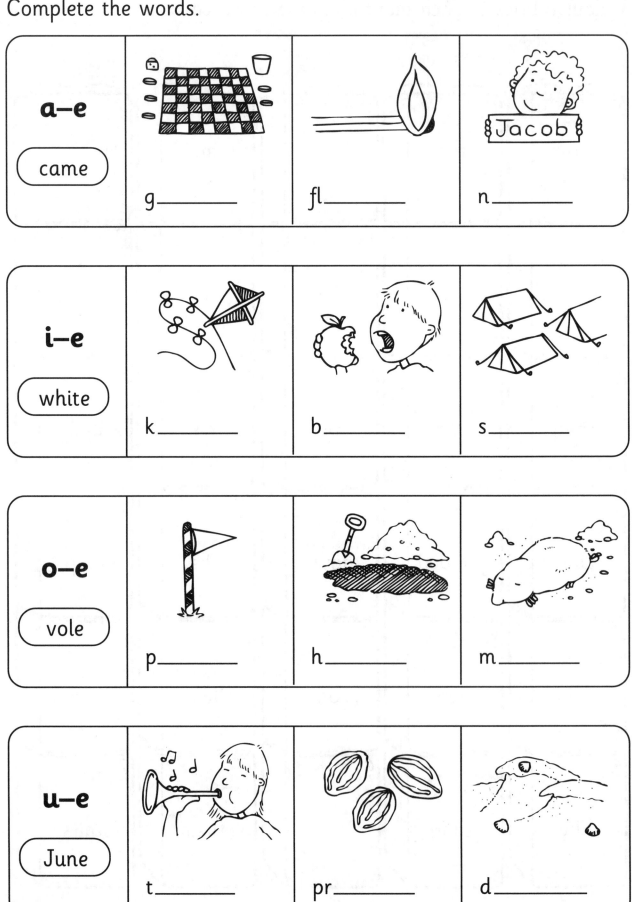

a–e

(came)

g_____   fl_____   n_____

i–e

(white)

k_____   b_____   s_____

o–e

(vole)

p_____   h_____   m_____

u–e

(June)

t_____   pr_____   d_____

Capital beginnings

Choose the capital letter to begin these sentences.

 i I ☐ live in a house.

 d D ☐ aisy lives in a flat.

 s S ☐ am lives in a caravan.

 m M ☐ y dog bites.

 i I ☐ lost my tooth.

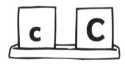 c C ☐ an I play?

 s S ☐ ally had a bath.

 h H ☐ er cat smells.

Capital titles

Put capital letters in the right places.

miss mills

_____iss _____ills

mrs toddy

_____rs _____oddy

mr green

_____r _____reen

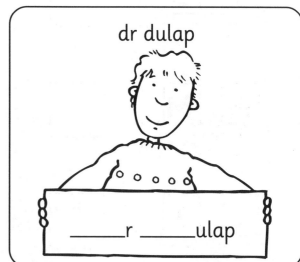

dr dulap

_____r _____ulap

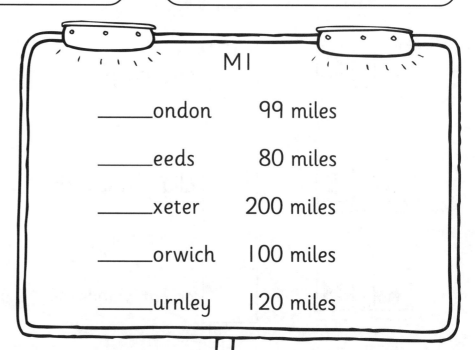

M1

london	_____ondon	99 miles
leeds	_____eeds	80 miles
exeter	_____xeter	200 miles
norwich	_____orwich	100 miles
burnley	_____urnley	120 miles

Missing titles

Write these titles on the books correctly. Don't forget capital letters.

paddington bear

little miss muffet

harry's mad

when the wind blows

mr tick the teacher

little red riding hood

Hands up!

Put question marks only after the questions.

May I go home

How old are you

Have you got a boyfriend

What time is it

I've got paint up my nose

I am hungry

Can I go to the loo

Story sense

Cut out the sentences and put them in the best order to make sense.

She walked home with the pail of milk.

Mary milked the cow.

Moo! The cow waited to be milked in the shed.

The cat drank the milk.

Mary poured some milk into a saucer.

The cat saw her coming.

Rick Wrong and Rose Right

What would Rose write? Write the correct sentences.

| my shoes put I on. | |
| I put my shoes on. | |

| my bed makes My mum for me. | |
| | |

| my boots ate Fido. | |
| | |

| going Are school to you? | |
| | |

| the TV sat on Dad it broke and. | |
| | |

| the bath sings in Aunt Jean. | |
| | |

| down Sit to lunch your eat. | |
| | |

Bookshelf

● Put the objects back into the right books.

● Make up your own book title and drawing.

MATHS

We have created these worksheets to support some essential elements in the National Numeracy Strategy, following the principles set down in the introduction to this book. Within the 45 minutes to an hour specified for mathematics lessons in primary schools, there is a heavy bias towards whole-class teaching and oral work, particularly with younger children. Nevertheless, within the *Framework for Teaching Mathematics*, there is also a place for individual work, for recording mathematics and for tackling written problems. The worksheets have a part to play here.

The following sheets are not a substitute for oral work or mental calculation, but they are intended to work as part of 'a balanced diet'. Differentiation is a growing problem as children continue to develop at varying rates and ability gaps widen, and it may sometimes be necessary to seek a solution by referring to material prepared for a younger (or older) age group. Differentiation in relation to Year 1 children is frequently determined by input, which, in practice, is really differentiation by time allocation – which means providing more adult support for the less able child. Although alternative activities are sometimes suggested for children of differing abilities, this form of differentiation is likely to be the most effective. Note that the extension activities, although sometimes consolidation, can constitute differentiation for the more able child.

Football numbers (page 50)

Objective: To know the number names in order and to count reliably.

What to do: The children can work alone to fill in the missing shirt numbers and also count the boots unaided. The shirts are in numerical order. The children can identify the number nine shirt in any way (by a circle or tick and so on). Where adult support is provided, challenge the children orally to identify this shirt before numbering all the shirts. The boots on the line is a straightforward counting exercise.

Differentiation: With a simple exercise such as this, differentiation will be by input. Discussion is essential to establish the real extent of a child's numerical competence. Ask: *Which shirt comes before the number nine shirt? Which is the next shirt?* and so on. Discuss why there is no shirt before number one. Use the words *zero*, *nought*, and *none*.

Extension: Enlarge the sheet. Cut out the numbered shirts. Ask the children to lay them out in the correct numerical order. *How many boots are there? How many boots would 12 players need?* Get the children to link the boots in pairs. *How many pairs of boots are there?*

How many? (page 51)

Objective: To count reliably sets of objects in different arrangements.

What to do: Children should count the objects in each different set, then write their answers in the boxes. The objects are deliberately set out in different arrangements and the children will need a counting or recording strategy to avoid miscounting and double counting. (There are 20 flowers, 13 cups and 11 sweets.)

Differentiation: Help those children that need support by teaching them a strategy to avoid miscounting – marking off each object counted, for example. Children might colour each object and number them as they do. Less able children may require sets of fewer objects to count (see 'Mathematical Development' in the Reception book in this series, photocopiable pages 63–6).

Extension: Get the children to make up counting sets of their own, either by drawing on paper, or using objects and apparatus. Perhaps they could make a counting set for a friend. Get another friend to check their answer. Using similar numbers of objects, encourage more able children to seek quick ways of counting, for example counting in twos.

Jumping in tens (page 52)

Objective: To extend number sequences counting backwards and forwards in tens.

What to do: The frog, kangaroo, bee and rabbit illustrate the jumping aspect of counting, and those children who understand this principle should have no difficulty in completing the steps by filling in the blanks. First they need to measure the size of the jumps (they are all tens) by counting if necessary.

Differentiation: Some children will need the support of a number line to manage this exercise. If there is not one on the classroom wall, children should have their own line on their desks. Encourage the children to use a number line when counting. Let them make the jumps along a line using a toy animal prop to reinforce the action if necessary.

Extension: Extend the jumping sequences – you might even attach an extra piece of paper to the photocopiable by way of extension. Challenge children to make their own jumping sequences in tens (give them the starting point). Practise counting in tens out loud. The latter might provide a useful exercise to be carried out at home although you will need to prepare clear instructions for parents to follow.

Odds and evens (page 53)

Objectives: To count in twos and to begin to recognise odd and even numbers.

What to do: The photocopiable sheet requires the children to count in twos, colouring every other number. This will result in two number strips – one showing odd numbers and one, even numbers. The first two in each sequence have been completed but instruct the children to start from the beginning each time. As part of this activity, children should count out loud and rhythmically, in twos starting at 2. Variations on this can include counting rhymes that also use the twos sequence. Children should also try counting in twos starting at 1. They should manage to get to at least 20. There are also two series of numbers on the sheet for the children to complete – also requiring them to count in twos.

Differentiation: Although most children will manage the colouring exercise, they may not all manage the oral sequence and these children will require repeated oral practice, preferably in small groups. When completing the sequences below the number strips, encourage less able children to use the number strips as an aid, making the jumps with their fingers or using pencil lines.

Extension: Encourage children to spot odd and even numbers out of sequence. *How old are you? Is this an odd or even number? Who lives in an even numbered house? Is the date an odd or even number?* Challenge more able children to explain how they can tell which is which. The most obvious extension activity is expansion – continue the number line. Can they complete the odd and even numbers to 50? Children could complete this at home.

Missing numbers (page 54)

Objective: To count on or back in steps of any size.
What to do: This will be a challenging exercise for most children. To complete the blanks they will need to be confident at counting on or back orally in twos,

fives, and threes and/or competent at counting on or back using a number line. Draw the children's attention to the small number line that has been provided as an aid, although if the class has a large number line they may prefer to use that.

Differentiation: Here the focus is on the number patterns of 2, 3, and 5. These number patterns can be reinforced using bricks, counters, lines and other counting apparatus. Less confident children might colour in these patterns on the given number line as an aid. Ask more able children to describe each sequence and challenge them to extend it.

Extension: As with the previous sheet, the most useful extension activities are repeated oral reinforcement and physical extension of the set sequences.

Writing numbers (page 55)

Objective: To read and write numbers in figures and words.

What to do: Introduce the children to the photocopiable sheet by going through the completed example at the top of the sheet. The dominoes are there simply as a counting aid and the children do not need to do anything with them other than (perhaps) colouring them for decorative purposes. Get the children to count the spots, check the numerals, then read the number. The children should fill in the blanks with numerals or words (the latter using the vocabulary provided at the bottom of the sheet where necessary). Note that there are more words at the bottom of the sheet than the children will need.

Differentiation: You will need to give support to the less able readers and, as an aid, it may help to produce a number line that has both numerals and words. This sheet concentrates on the 'teens' but if the children are not confident in reading and writing these numbers, then devise a simpler sheet using smaller numbers for them to use.

Extension: Exercise and consolidate the children's ability to read numbers by using simple games. Hold up cards with numerals on them and ask children to say what they are. Do the same using words. Get children to point at named numbers in the classroom (computer keyboard, number line, clock face, telephone and so on). Encourage the children to practise number naming at home.

Tens and ones (page 56)

Objective: To be able to partition a number into tens and ones.

What to do: Ideally, the children should use a real abacus along with this sheet so that they can manipulate the numbers physically. (Every classroom should possess this equipment. Usually they have four 'towers' but for this exercise children need only use two. Label the columns if necessary.) Explain the completed example. Children can then complete the remainder. On finishing the sheet, provide oral follow-up, with the children explaining the answers. *What does the 1 stand for in 13?* And so on.

Differentiation: Dienes (multi-base) apparatus, or similar (base ten), provides an excellent way of demonstrating number values in an understandable way, and you might want to use it with those children who have difficulty in understanding how a single counter can represent a ten. For those who have mastered the principle (that is, place value), reverse the process. For example, give the child thirteen counters (all the same colour) and get them to change them into tens and units on the abacus.

Extension: The principle of place value will require a great deal of consolidation. Give the children more practice along the lines of the photocopiable, then using an abacus or Dienes apparatus, get them to reverse the process – converting units (or *ones* – both terms should be used) into tens and ones. The next sheet provides more practice.

More tens and ones (page 57)

Objective: To be able to partition a number into tens and ones.

What to do: Confident children who have managed the previous sheet will find this one useful consolidation and will enjoy demonstrating their skill and knowledge. Those who are still not confident at this stage should tackle the sheet using apparatus (abacus or Dienes).

Differentiation/extension: See 'Tens and ones' above.

Number splits (page 58)

Objective: To be able to partition a number into tens and ones and into multiples of tens and ones.

What to do: The children need to split the numbers into tens and units. You should perhaps first explain the joke of the clown doing the splits and then proceed to the exercise!

Differentiation: The children might find the notion that

the numbers consist of tens and ones difficult to grasp. You might try photo-enlarging the clown and then repeating the number splits exercise by writing the numbers on the clown's feet (they can be stuck on using Post-it Notes or similar). The children will enjoy playing this game for themselves solving each box using the clown's feet.

Extension: Children will certainly need lots of reinforcement of this concept, so more of the same is called for. Extend the range of tens used. Some children will cope with hundreds and multiples of hundred and therefore will be able to split numbers three ways (HTUs).

In the queue (page 59)

Objective: To use and understand the vocabulary of ordering numbers and to use ordinal numbers.

What to do: Preliminary work is necessary here. Either as individuals or as a class exercise, the children need to count objects (such as these animals) and hear and use the vocabulary of ordering. *Who is last in the queue? Who is first, third and so on?* Note that the children need to start from a fixed point – in this case the bus stop. Either get the children to copy the words into the spaces, or teach them the shorthand version. The most important thing is that the children can use the words correctly.

Differentiation: Filling in the blanks will be a difficult chore for some, so a supporting adult could assist children here. Using the language is the most important thing.

Extension: Why not get the children to add one or two animals of their own to the queue and then add sentences of their own? A nice challenge is to reverse the queue by placing the bus stop at the other end. Do the answers to the questions change? This could form a follow-up activity for homework.

More than... (page 60)

Objective: To learn to say the number that is one or ten more than any given number up to 30.

What to do: As with the previous photocopiable, it is more important that the children can respond orally to the problems rather than being able to write the answers down. All of these examples can be completed orally, perhaps as a class or group exercise (you can make a game of it) before the sheet is presented for individual completion.

Differentiation: Apart from adult support, give less confident children counting apparatus to support them. Show them how to solve the problems using a number line. Use money to create 'more than' problems. The more practice the better.

Extension: Practical problems are the next step. Pose

some: *Yesterday there were 20 children for dinner; today we have one more child. How many dinners will we need?; An apple costs 25p, and an orange costs 10p more than an apple. How much is an orange?*

Less than... (page 61)

Objective: To learn to say the number that is one or ten less than any given number up to 30.

What to do: Use exactly the same procedure as for the 'More than…' sheet. First carry out oral work. You might have some fun talking to the children about the talking scarecrows. You may want to photo-enlarge the scarecrows as teaching apparatus.

Differentiation/extension: See 'More than…' above.

Five faces (page 62)

Objective: To begin to know addition facts for all pairs of numbers with a total of up to at least 5.

What to do: The children should colour in the five faces in such a way that the combination matches the arithmetical equation on the right of the sheet. They should choose two colours, one for each number in the equation. Obviously they will only need to use one colour where the equation contains a zero! Explain the first two examples with the children. When the exercise is complete, ask the children to explain (in groups or as a whole class), out loud, what the coloured faces show.

Differentiation: Children could repeat this activity using bricks, or other apparatus, if it helps. Support less able children with lots of discussion. For those who find the colouring exercise a particular chore, they can stick gummed circles onto the faces instead.

Extension: When the sheet is complete, ask the children to demonstrate the number patterns in another way using Lego bricks, Unifix cubes and so on. The next two sheets complement this one and can be used as extension work. Clearly this format

can be used for other numbers under ten and therefore you can ask the children to make up their own faces (or similar) to 'tell the story' of seven, eight and so on. Where you are confident that the children understand the concept, they can complete these activities at home.

Six sailors (page 63)

Objective: To begin to know addition facts for all pairs of numbers with a total up to at least 10.

What to do: This is a variation on the previous sheet, only this time there are no completed examples and the children will need to devise a strategy for making up the combination of numbers to six. More able children may manage without reference to the sailors; others should use them for counting and for marking off completed number sentences.

Differentiation/extension: See 'Five faces' above.

Ten tumblers (page 64)

Objective: To begin to know addition facts for all pairs of numbers up to 10.

What to do: This is simply a more challenging variation on the previous activity, 'Six sailors' and can be approached in the same way. Again, encourage those who need to, to use the tumblers as a counting aid.

Differentiation/extension: See 'Five faces' above.

Size order (page 65)

Objective: To order a set of familiar numbers saying which is smaller or larger.

What to do: Tell the children to put the flowerpots in order of size – first a row going from largest to smallest, then a row putting the smallest number first. They will find it easier to order the numbers and write them on the flowerpots first, before drawing.

Differentiation: You will certainly need to give oral instructions to the children, and less able children will need more of such support. It would help to physically work out a similar example using bricks or other objects first. Show them what they need to write. For those who still struggle, the pictures can be cut out and arranged in order. Repeat, using any equipment available.

Extension: Play the ordering numbers game using playing cards, sums of money or coins, classroom objects such as piles of books and so on. Using a handful of playing cards or numbered cards, get the children to order them, then to shuffle them for a friend to do the exercise. Give each child a small number of cards to take home. Ask them to sort them into order (largest first, then smallest first) and record their answers.

Sorting sheep (page 66)

Objective: To order a set of familiar numbers.

What to do: It will not be immediately self-evident to the children what they need to do with this sheet so you will need to go through it with them first. The object of the exercise is to travel, in order, from the largest flock of sheep down to the smallest. First the children need to count the sheep and to write the number of sheep in each field into the blank boxes provided. The largest flock has been completed for them. After counting the sheep, they should then take a coloured pencil and, starting with the largest flock, draw a line from field to field joining the numbers in the boxes in size order, finishing with the smallest flock of sheep. They may find it more fun, although a little more difficult, to go from field to field using the gates only.

Differentiation: To put the activity into context, tell a story about a farmer counting his sheep, looking for a lost sheep, inspecting for foot and mouth, and so on. Remember that the children need to understand that they are ranking the numbers in size order starting with the largest. Less able children should talk about the walk around the fields with an adult. They can then trace the walk with their finger before they make marks on the sheet.

Extension: For more practice, once the children understand the idea of the sheet, simply alter the number of sheep in the fields by adding more sheep and reuse the photocopiable at home or in the classroom.

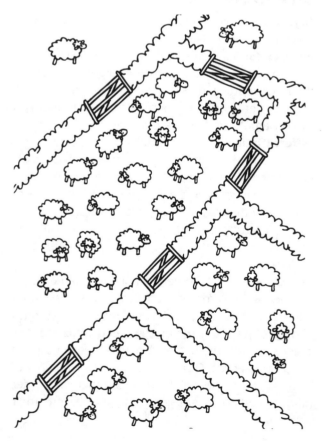

Three jumps to 6 (page 67)

Objective: To understand addition as steps along a number line.

What to do: The first example on the sheet has been completed. Talk this through with children so that they understand the process. (Ideally this will not be a one-off experience and the children will have used this strategy on the classroom number line, orally, and with the whole class before doing this sheet.) Use the terms *sum, total, add, altogether, equals* and *sign* when talking with the children about the example. The children should then use the blank number lines to show three more ways of making 6, recording the jumps on the line and then writing the number sentence next to it.

Differentiation: Any strategy that makes the jumping along the line memorable is worth using. Less able children could use a small toy to make the jumps, recording each jump as it is made. They must understand that they can only make three jumps and must reach 6 at the end. No repetitions – they must show three different ways of reaching 6.

Extension: The next sheet gives an example of how you can extend this activity; not only can you make the final destination a higher number, but you can increase the number of jumps. You can also reverse the process – give children a number sentence and ask them to record it as a series of jumps (this could be done at home).

Three jumps to 10 (page 68)

Objective: To understand addition as steps along a number line.

What to do: This is an extension of the idea shown in 'Three jumps to 6' above.

Differentiation/extension: See above. As a challenge, ask the children to find four ways to make 10. *How many different ways can you do this?*

Blank arithmetic (page 69)

Objective: To record simple additions in a number sentence that includes + and = signs, using a number line as an aid.

What to do: By the time children use this sheet they should be familiar with using number lines. Remind them how to add using a number line (making jumps). They should then carry out each addition on the line on the sheet and record the total in each blank square. Make sure they understand what the blank stands for.

Differentiation: For less able children you should simplify the recording of the jumps by allowing them to mark each jump on the line. To avoid confusion you will either need many blank lines, a plastic number line that allows each sum to be marked and then removed, or some other similar strategy.

Extension: Give more able children similar number sentences where the blank square represents a number other than the total. For example $3 + \square = 8$. Pose this question orally at first. *If I start on 3, how many jumps do I have to make to reach 8?* They can make up their own number sentences and find answers to them. Many children will simply need more practice of the same.

More blank arithmetic (page 70)

Objective: To recognise that $\square$ and $\triangle$ stand for unknown numbers and use this knowledge to complete number sentences containing blanks.

What to do: Explaining how to make jumps on a number line should be easy as the children should by now have had plenty of practice at carrying out this operation. However, this photocopiable sheet makes a significant and, for some, a difficult step. The children need to understand that in any given number sentence, the symbols $\square$ and $\triangle$ cannot represent the same number. The more observant children will catch on to the fact that where two identical symbols are used in one sentence, they must be identical numbers. This is not an easy idea for children to grasp, you will appreciate why if you consider that they are really doing simple algebra in the form $x + y = 8$ or $x + x = 8$ or $y + y = 8$.

Differentiation: Understanding that the triangle and square cannot be the same number is the key to completing this sheet successfully. Less able children will need to go over this many times. Carry out the exercise using a large flip chart or board so that the symbols are clearly large blanks to be filled. Alternatively, you might use large plastic shapes and write the numbers on them as the sums are completed by the class. Demonstrate that the numbers can only be the same if the shapes will fit exactly on each other.

Extension: Once the children grasp the principle they should be able to make up number sentences of their own with little difficulty. They could do this at home.

Spending money (page 71)

Objective: To use addition to solve money problems.

What to do: If you practise similar problems orally, the children should be able to carry out these addition sums mentally. Do this using small numbers. As each example on the sheet involves using money, you may want to provide the children with coins. Demonstrate what they have to do and where they need to record the totals.

Differentiation: Devise an easier form of the problem by simply reducing the values given. Unfortunately, the problems will lose a degree of realism as there is

very little that can be purchased for pennies these days – you will not get a cornet for 2p!

Extension: The best extension activities are probably oral (not recommended to be set for homework). Challenge children to add mentally three small numbers up to about 12. Reverse the process and ask *Can you say three numbers that add up to 7?* If you want to practise using money, the traditional method of shopping in the class shop is as good a way as any. Encourage parents to allow children to handle and cope with money in small amounts and to involve them in simple shopping problems.

Dodgem puzzles (page 72)

Objective: To recognise that more than two numbers can be added together.

What to do: Make sure that the children are clear about choosing three digits. They should not choose to add $94 + 5 + 1$, for example. Demonstrate the example on the sheet to the children. They should choose three digits from the number plates of the dodgems to make different totals, for example $9 + 5 + 1 = 10$; $9 + 4 + 5 = 18$. How many totals can they make in this way?

Differentiation: Recording the number sentences may pose problems for some and these children will need adult help. If the addition itself proves to be a problem then provide apparatus – any counting aid, bricks, number line and so on will be useful.

Extension: Get children to make up similar problems for themselves. They could draw the number plates of two cars in the school car park or in the street at home. Those with more than one family vehicle can make up examples using their own cars – quite an interesting homework problem.

Find the difference (page 73)

Objective: To consolidate knowledge of subtraction using the term *the difference between*.

What to do: If this sheet follows much oral and practical work on finding the difference between two numbers, then the sheet itself will need very little explanation.

Otherwise, as 'difference' in arithmetic has a concrete existence, use sets of counters and bricks to compare numbers, so that the children can see, count and hold 'the difference'. The children should write their answers in the boxes at the side of each example.

Differentiation: If children are finding this difficult, demonstrate the strategy of one-to-one matching. Taking the first example, if they mark off each balloon in the left hand with a corresponding balloon in the right hand then any balloons left unmarked will show the difference between the two numbers. Children can continue using this strategy with the birds, coins, kittens and flies.

Extension: Children may use counting on or taking away to find the difference. Get the children to respond rapidly to oral questions that involve simple subtraction. Pose them in a variety of ways: *Take 3 from 7. What number must I take from 7 to leave 4? I think of a number. I take away 4. My answer is 3. What is my number?* You can, of course, extend the activity by making the quantities bigger but it is more valuable to develop mental agility.

Guess Nelly's numbers (page 74)

Objective: To consolidate knowledge of subtraction, using the terms *taking away* and *subtract*.

What to do: Like the previous sheet, this again involves subtraction but using different vocabulary and the operation of complementary addition. Show those children who cannot see the process for themselves, how adding back what was taken away gets you back to the quantity that you started with. Tell them to record their answers on the cards held in Nelly's hands.

Differentiation: Demonstrate the exercise using bricks with less able children. Get them to handle the 3 taken away and the 7 left. Ask them: *If I had not taken the 3 away, how many would there be?* Provide lots of hands-on experience for those lacking the mental ability to cope with the exercise.

Extension: See 'Find the difference' above.

Seeing double (page 75)

Objective: To begin to use and know by heart the addition doubles of numbers up to 6.

What to do: Go through the completed example with the children. Use the term *double*. Challenge the children to remember the answers.

Differentiation: As the numbers are small, the children should not have any trouble with the counting. Less able children can find the total by counting on if necessary.

Extension: A fun exercise is to let the children draw their own pictures to double. This would make a good challenge for children to tackle at home.

How much is this? (page 76)

Objectives: To add numbers (using knowledge of doubles) using money. To recognise coins of different values.

What to do: Talk through the completed example on the sheet with the children. Tell them they must simply add together the value of the coins to find the total. They can write down the quantities and do the addition by any appropriate means. However, if you have carried out sufficient oral work on 'doubles', then encourage the children to look for doubles and to use their knowledge of them to work out the answers mentally and then record the total. Make sure that children have the opportunity to play with and recognise the coins used. Use real money wherever possible.

Differentiation: Used in its most basic way this is simply a straightforward addition exercise and for those who can only cope on that level then that is how the sheet will be used. These children could use coins or counters to assist them in finding the totals. However, try and stretch most children into using mental strategies such as doubles. If children are more able, demand the answers without the written sum.

Extension: Sticking to the money theme, give the children a few coins to total as quickly as possible. They could do this in groups – give each child the same number of coins and then they have to race to find the total. Encourage them to look for 'short-cuts'. To beef up the addition for more able children, provide examples that extend the number or range of coins.

Time passing (page 77)

Objective: To solve simple problems involving time.

What to do: How you use this sheet will depend upon the maturity and ability of the children. For some children, present them as word problems such as *I get up at 8 o'clock and go to school at 9 o'clock. How long is that?* and so on. Even when doing the sheet in this manner, the children should follow the problems on the sheet, observing the times shown on the clocks. Show them where to write their answers. Those children who are competent at telling the time should be able to cope without support. The presence of the drawings eliminates the am/pm possibility.

Differentiation: This sheet is already differentiated by the use of both words and pictures and by treating it as a diagrammatic/written exercise where a child can read clock time.

Extension: In class, give children more practice of the same or similar. Ideally, use a class clock with hands that can be manipulated properly (some sort of gearing is required – cardboard non-linked hands are not so good). For homework, pose one or two 'find out' problems, such as *At what time does Daddy go to work? How many hours are there from when school finishes to when EastEnders starts?*

Sorting shapes (page 78)

Objective: To describe properties of 2-D shapes.

What to do: Carry out lots of oral and practical work with shapes before tackling this sheet. Make sure the children first understand the language. Can they identify a side? A corner? Can they tell the difference between a long side and a short side? Once they have worked out how many sides and corners each shape has, they can complete the blanks.

Differentiation: Differentiate by input. Give less able children the help of a supporting adult. If you have similar 2-D plastic or wooden shapes, then the children can handle these. If not, cut out each shape and mount them on card so that the children can feel the sides and touch the corners.

Extension: Use attribute blocks to sort shapes into sets by attribute. The precision of attribution must depend upon the ability of the child. Get the children to draw a round shape. (Challenge: how will they do this?) Discuss how it differs from the shapes on the sheet.

Where am I? (page 79)

Objective: To use everyday language to describe positions.

What to do: This is a hunt-the-mouse exercise where children need to find the mouse in each picture. This will have little value if the children simply point, so carry out oral work. You can enlarge the sheet and use it as a group teaching aid. If the children work as individuals, it is still essential that they describe what they see orally – so an adult will need to be involved. Get the children to use the word labels at the bottom of the sheet to label the pictures as appropriate. They may cut out and stick the labels or draw a line to join the labels to the pictures.

Differentiation: Some children will do this activity orally, but more able children may read and use the words given at the bottom of the sheet. Note that more words are provided than needed and that in some cases there is more than one correct answer. Children can play the position game for real with a toy mouse or amusing substitute. *Who can see where the mouse is hiding this morning children?*

Extension: More able children might, assisted or unaided, write a sentence about the position of the mouse in each picture by selecting words from the vocabulary provided. If you have a floor robot, use it to elicit positional descriptions from children.

Repeating patterns (page 80)

Objective: To be able to make and describe repeating patterns of shapes.

What to do: Make sure that the children realise that each new line signifies the start of a new pattern. Get the children to point to and describe each shape in turn – *square, triangle, rectangle, circle. When does the sequence repeat itself? What shape comes next?* Tell them to continue drawing the sequence in the blanks provided.

Differentiation: Help less able children to see the sequence by getting them to colour each shape a different colour. However, it is important that when describing the sequence you encourage them to use the words describing shape. More able children should cope with making a sequence of their own in the space provided at the bottom of the sheet. Get them to stand up and describe the sequence to other children.

Extension: Challenge the children to make up two repeating patterns and then swap them with a friend. *Can you complete each other's patterns?*

Football numbers

● Fill in the missing shirt numbers. Which is the number 9 shirt?

● How many boots are there?

How many?

Count the objects and write down how many there are in the boxes.

[ ] flowers

[ ] sweets

[ ] cups

Jumping in tens

Complete the jumps for the animals by filling in the numbers.

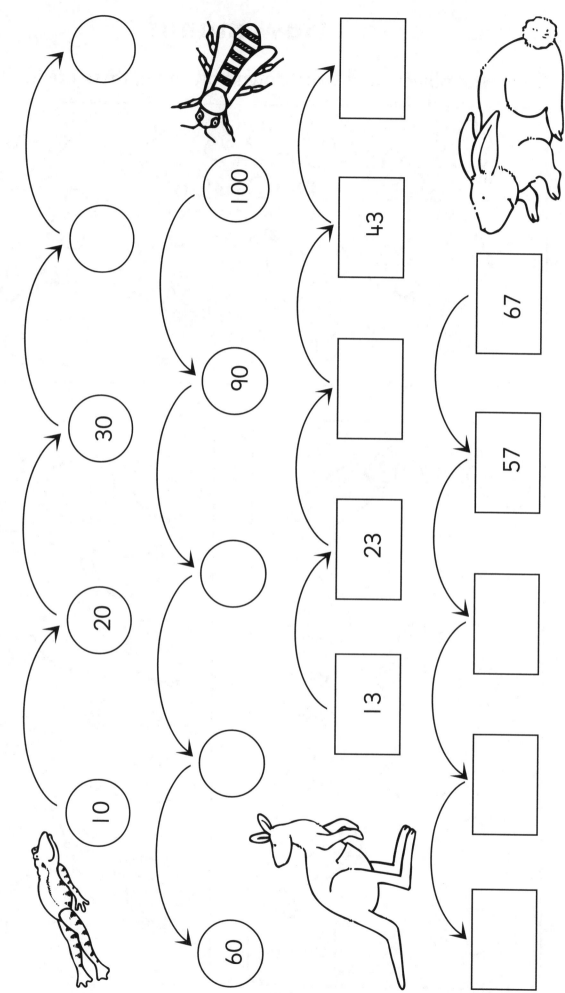

Odds and evens

● Colour every other number. Start with 1.

| 1 | 2 | 3 | 4 | 5 | 6 | 7 | 8 | 9 | 10 | 11 | 12 | 13 | 14 | 15 | 16 | 17 | 18 | 19 | 20 |

● Colour every other number. Start with 2.

| 1 | 2 | 3 | 4 | 5 | 6 | 7 | 8 | 9 | 10 | 11 | 12 | 13 | 14 | 15 | 16 | 17 | 18 | 19 | 20 |

● Which numbers come next?

10, 12, 14, 16, , ,

17, 15, 13, 11,

Missing numbers

Finish the number sequences by filling in the blanks.

5,   10,   15,   ☐ ,   ☐

2,   4,   6,   ☐ ,   ☐

3,   6,   9,   ☐ ,   ☐

2,   4,   6,   ☐ ,   10,   ☐

10,   15,   ☐ ,   25,   ☐ ,   ☐

3,   6,   ☐ ,   12,   ☐ ,   ☐

30,   25,   ☐ ,   15,   ☐ ,   ☐

22,   20,   ☐ ,   16,   ☐ ,   ☐

Writing numbers

Fill in the gaps with numerals or words.

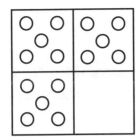 → 15 → fifteen

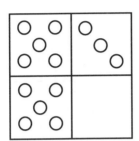 → 13 → [ ]

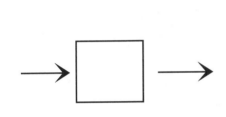 → [ ] → eleven

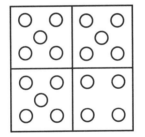 → 19 → [ ]

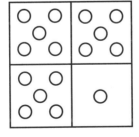 → 16 → [ ]

| thirteen | sixteen | nineteen |
| eleven | fifteen | seventeen |

Tens and ones

Write down how many tens and ones are on the abacus.

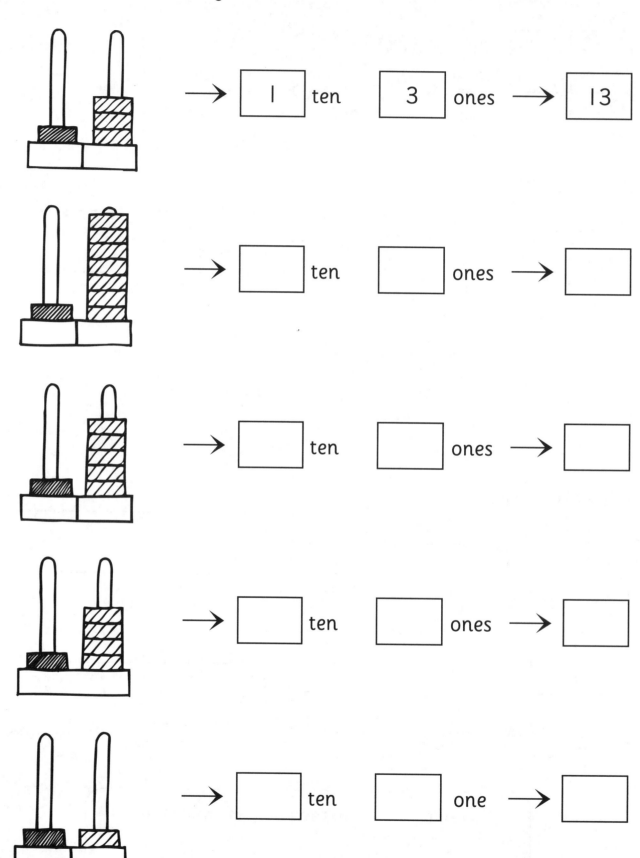

→ [1] ten [3] ones → [13]

→ [ ] ten [ ] ones → [ ]

→ [ ] ten [ ] ones → [ ]

→ [ ] ten [ ] ones → [ ]

→ [ ] ten [ ] one → [ ]

More tens and ones

Write down how many tens and ones make up these numbers.

13 → | 1 | ten | 3 | ones

10 → | | ten | | ones

19 → | | ten | | ones

11 → | | ten | | one

20 → | | tens | | ones

16 → | | ten | | ones

12 → | | ten | | ones

18 → | | ten | | ones

17 → | | ten | | ones

15 → | | ten | | ones

14 → | | ten | | ones

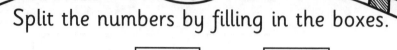

Number splits

Split the numbers by filling in the boxes.

14 = ☐ + ☐

12 = ☐ + 2

17 = 10 + ☐

13 = ☐ + 3

18 = ☐ + 8

10 = 10 + ☐

23 = 20 + ☐

28 = ☐ + 8

35 = ☐ + 5

47 = 40 + ☐

In the queue

● Who comes where in the queue?

first   second   third   fourth   fifth   sixth

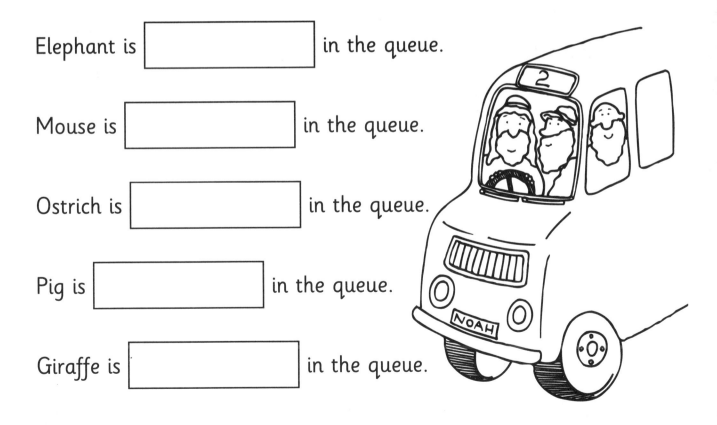

Elephant is ⬚ in the queue.

Mouse is ⬚ in the queue.

Ostrich is ⬚ in the queue.

Pig is ⬚ in the queue.

Giraffe is ⬚ in the queue.

● Who is last in the queue? _____

More than...

I've got one more than you!

One more than 6 is 7

One more than 16 is

One more than 4 is

One more than 12 is

One more than 9 is

One more than 25 is

One more than 13 is

One more than 27 is

One more than 19 is

One more than 18 is

One more than 24 is

Less than...

One less than 7 is $\boxed{6}$

One less than 17 is $\boxed{}$

One less than 24 is $\boxed{}$

One less than 4 is $\boxed{}$

One less than 28 is $\boxed{}$

One less than 8 is $\boxed{}$

One less than 30 is $\boxed{}$

One less than 25 is $\boxed{}$

One less than 22 is $\boxed{}$

One less than 20 is $\boxed{}$

One less than 16 is $\boxed{}$

Five faces

Colour in the faces to match the sums on the right.

$0 + 5 = 5$

$1 + 4 = 5$

$2 + 3 = 5$

$3 + 2 = 5$

$4 + 1 = 5$

$5 + 0 = 5$

Six sailors

6 = [   ] + 6

6 = [   ] + 5

6 = [   ] + 4

6 = [   ] + 3

6 = [   ] + 2

6 = [   ] + 1

6 = [   ] + 0

Ten tumblers

$10 = \boxed{} + 0$

$10 = \boxed{} + 6$

$10 = \boxed{} + 1$

$10 = \boxed{} + 7$

$10 = \boxed{} + 2$

$10 = \boxed{} + 8$

$10 = \boxed{} + 3$

$10 = \boxed{} + 9$

$10 = \boxed{} + 4$

$10 = \boxed{} + 10$

$10 = \boxed{} + 5$

Size order

● Look at the pots above. Draw the flowers in the pots below, ordering them from largest to smallest.

● Now order them from smallest to largest.

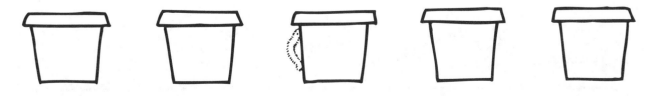

Sorting sheep

● How many sheep are in each field? Write your answers in the boxes.

● Then draw a line connecting the boxes, starting with the largest flock and finishing with the smallest.

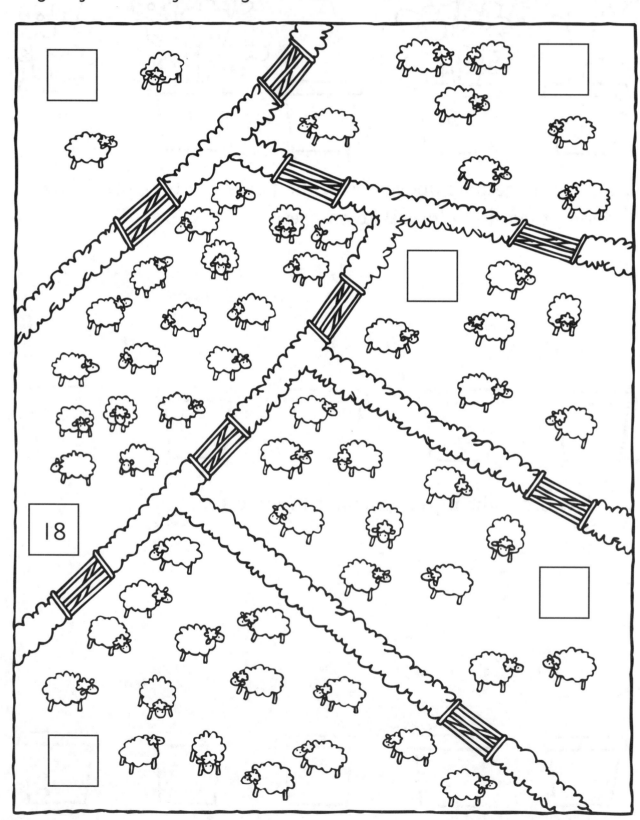

Three jumps to 6

- How can you get to **6** in three jumps?

$$1 + 1 + 4 = 6$$

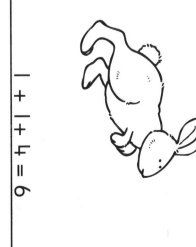

- Now make three more of your own.

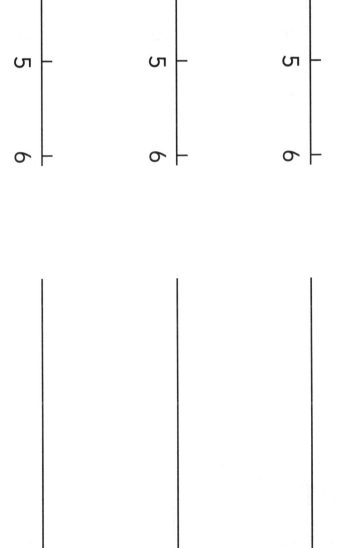

Three jumps to 10

● How can you get to **10** in three jumps?

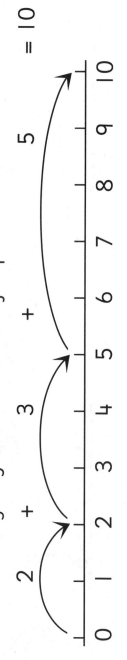

$2 + 3 + 5 = 10$

● Now make three more of your own.

$2 + 3 + 5 = 10$

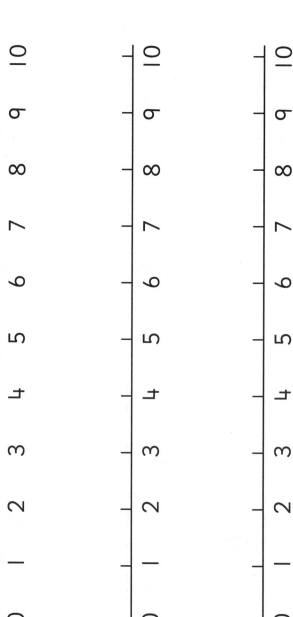

Use the number line to help you fill in the blanks.

Blank arithmetic

3 + 3 =

1 + 8 =

5 + 6 =

12 + 3 =

16 + 4 =

12 + 5 =

11 + 7 =

17 + 6 =

14 + 8 =

19 + 6 =

More blank arithmetic

- Look at how this sum can be made.

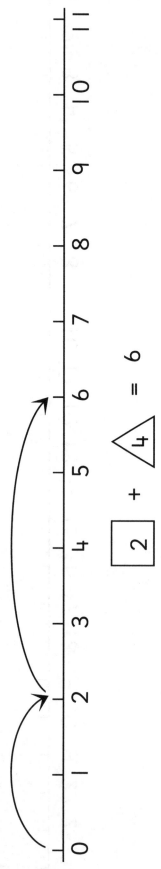

$$2 + 4 = 6$$

- Now make up your own sums.

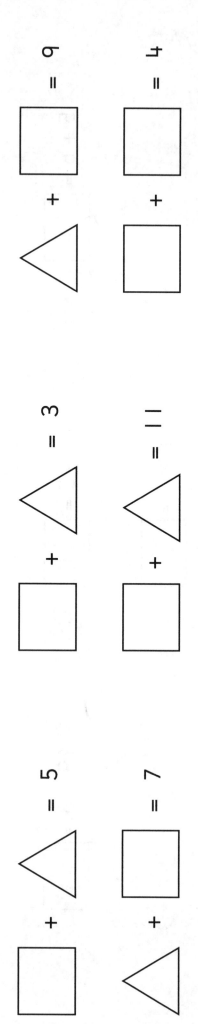

$$\square + \triangle = 5$$

$$\triangle + \square = 3$$

$$\triangle + \square = 9$$

$$\square + \square = 7$$

$$\square + \triangle = 11$$

$$\square + \square = 4$$

Spending money

How much did these children spend?

20p

15p

10p

I bought one cornet for 10p.

I bought three cornets for _____ p.

I bought one lolly for 20p.

I bought three lollies for _____ p.

I bought one tub for 15p.

I bought two tubs for _____ p.

Dodgem puzzles

Choose three digits from each pair of dodgems.
What totals can you make each time?

| 9 | + | 4 | + | 1 | = | 14 |

☐ + ☐ + ☐ = ___

☐ + ☐ + ☐ = ___

☐ + ☐ + ☐ = ___

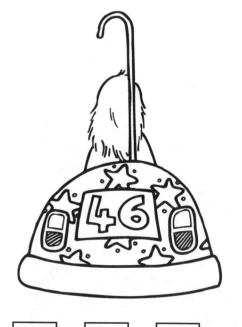

☐ + ☐ + ☐ = ___

☐ + ☐ + ☐ = ___

☐ + ☐ + ☐ = ___

☐ + ☐ + ☐ = ___

Find the difference

What is the difference between these groups of objects?
Write your answers in the boxes.

Guess Nelly's numbers

Nelly takes away 3
Her answer is 7
Nelly's number is:

Nelly takes away 2
Her answer is 4
Nelly's number is:

Nelly takes away 4
Her answer is 10
Nelly's number is:

Nelly subtracts 3
Her answer is 5
Nelly's number is:

Nelly subtracts 5
Her answer is 8
Nelly's number is:

Seeing double

toes		5	+	5	=	10
legs			+		=	
wheels			+		=	
ears			+		=	
noses			+		=	
spots			+		=	

How much is this?

- Add up the coins to find the total.
- Write the sum on the line.

$1p + 1p + 5p = 7p$

_____

_____

_____

_____

_____

_____

_____

Time passing

From 8 o'clock to 9 o'clock is _____ hour.

From 9 o'clock to 12 o'clock is _____ hours.

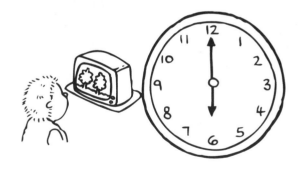

From 3 o'clock to 6 o'clock is _____ hours.

From 4 o'clock to 7 o'clock is _____ hours.

Sorting shapes

How many sides and corners does each shape have?
Write your answers in the circles.

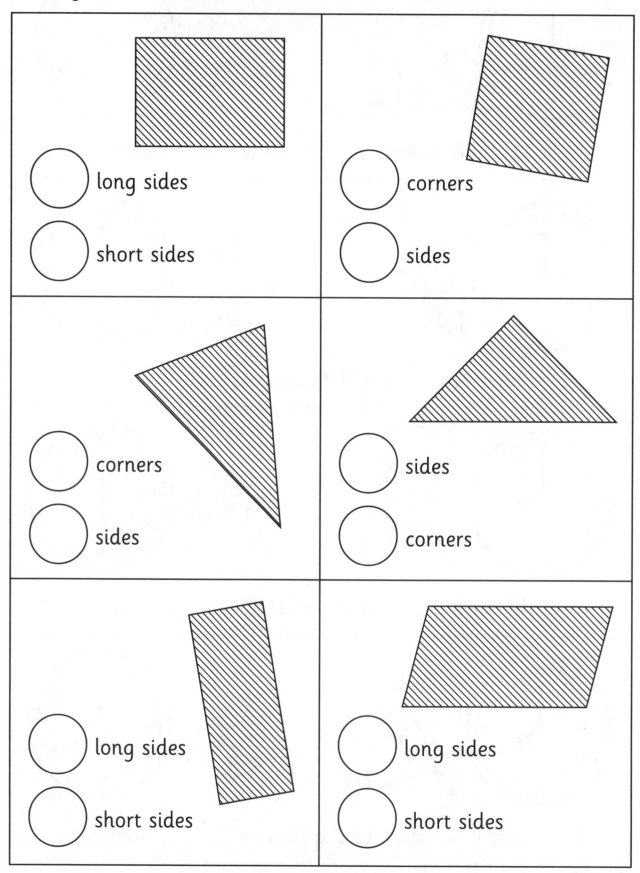

○ long sides

○ short sides

○ corners

○ sides

○ corners

○ sides

○ sides

○ corners

○ long sides

○ short sides

○ long sides

○ short sides

Where am I?

underneath   next to   inside   close to   near   on

above   outside   on top of   opposite   in front of

Repeating patterns

- Finish the patterns.

- Now make up your own pattern.

SCIENCE

In the National Curriculum document for science, there is an approach that is common to a number of subjects. On the one hand there is the identification of *skills*, and on the other, the identification of the *content* through which these skills are to be taught. Thus in science, the skills (scientific enquiry) are taught through the content (called 'contexts'). Although the scientific 'contexts' have been pared down since the National Curriculum was first conceived, there is still a great deal of science to be tackled even in Year 1. Fortunately, the nature of the subject matter, combined with agreed good practice for teaching infants, allows that there will be overlap between subjects. For example, when tackling the unit 'Ourselves' in the QCA Scheme of Work, one immediately becomes aware of resonance with both geography and history requirements. There is also a clear overlap between music and the scientific study of sound. Even so there is still a lot of science to be taught, and in order to give reasonable coverage, we have limited ourselves to the QCA Scheme of Work and those objectives that photocopiable worksheets are best able to support.

The National Curriculum science 'contexts' are 'Life processes and living things' (Sc2); 'Materials and their properties' (Sc3); and 'Physical processes' (Sc4). Sc1 ('Scientific enquiry'), sets out the skills and principles to be taught through the 'contexts'. The QCA scheme covers this ground in six units. The units are dealt with in the order: 'Ourselves'; 'Growing plants'; 'Sorting and using materials'; 'Light and dark'; 'Pushes and pulls'; 'Sound and hearing'. There is no attempt at comprehensive cover here, but the sheets do offer support to key elements in these units.

Body parts (page 86)

Objective: To be able to locate and name external parts of the human body.

What to do: On this photocopiable sheet, the children match the words to the parts of the body. The important thing is that they know the parts of the body (not that they read the words), so carry out a whole-class oral naming of parts before they attempt the activity. If you have displayed the words in the classroom, and if the children are familiar with them, then they should be able to complete the exercise unaided.

Differentiation: Less able children

will need more work on knowing the parts. Play games like 'Simon says', 'Touch your knee' and so on. Reading and matching the words may still be a problem – point out that the word shapes need to be matched and that this helps find the right word. An adult could cut out the words provided and the child then sticks them into the appropriate spaces.

Extension: Attempt more sophisticated identification. Ask the children to identify, for example, an earlobe, a shoulder blade, or an instep. Enlarge the sheet and use it for display purposes, adding key parts of the body for the children to learn.

Five senses (page 87)

Objective: To understand that we have five senses through which we learn about the world.

What to do: Children fill in the blanks after reading the sentence and looking for the word required from amongst the illustrations on the right.

Differentiation: Read out the sentences for less confident readers. Mime to the children what the senses are used for. If necessary, cut out the pictures on the right of the sheet and allow the children to stick the pictures into the blanks instead of writing the words.

Extension: There are all sorts of small experiments that can be carried out to encourage children to use and become aware of their senses, such as feeling objects in a feely bag, identifying sounds on a tape, and so on. Extension should be in the sphere of experimentation, testing and investigation.

Am I an animal?

(page 88)

Objective: To understand that the term 'animal' includes humans.

What to do: Explain to the children about the two categories, 'animal' and 'other', and the difference between them. Get the children to sort the pictures into the two categories, placing them in the appropriate set. They can do this either by using an arrow to link the drawing to the set or (more fun) by cutting out and sticking the pictures into the set. You can draw or photo-enlarge the sets if necessary.

Differentiation: Less able children should physically sort the pictures. Ask them questions about the pictures: *What is this called? Is it an animal? How can we tell?*

Extension: You will need to reinforce the notion that, in common with the slug, we are also animals. Examine categories of animals. Ask the children to investigate animals that are fish or insects. Ask them to name six of each category.

Adults and young (page 89)

Objectives: To match adults and young of the same animals and to understand that animals grow and change over time.

What to do: You need to explain that adult animals no longer grow. *Which of the pictures show adult animals? What did they used to be like before they grew into adult animals?* When children have teased out the answers to these questions, they should link the adult and young by drawing a line.

Differentiation: You will need to differentiate by giving lots of visual clues and hands-on support to less able children.

Extension: All children will benefit from seeing lots of images of young and adult animals. Firsthand experience is better still. Visit a farm or a zoo. Ask them questions, such as *Have you got any pets? Has anyone got a baby sister or brother? How have they changed since they were born?* Ask children to describe the changes. Perhaps they could bring photographs from home to illustrate how they have changed. Investigate growth by keeping height records of the children in the classroom. Let them measure themselves once a month. *Do we grow in ways other than in height?*

Alive and not alive (page 90)

Objective: To distinguish between animals and inanimate objects.

What to do: This sheet involves sorting into sets in the same way as the children did in 'Am I an animal?' above, but first they have to understand the categories. Explain to the children the differences between living and non-living things using the terms *feed*, *move* and *grow*.

Differentiation: Experience is the key to understanding here. Although some children may tackle this sheet with little introduction, others will need hands-on experience before attempting the sheet. Go on a 'nature' walk. Collect some living things (woodlice, snails) and non-living things (stones, crisp wrappers), sort them and talk about the differences.

Extension: Ask: *What do we need to stay alive?* (Food and drink.) Ask the children to describe how to look after a pet. *What do they feed it? What does it drink? How often does it need feeding?*

Plants around school (page 91)

Objectives: To learn that there are different plants in the immediate environment, and that plants have leaves, stems, and flowers.

What to do: Ideally children should walk round the school grounds or other suitable place (at the right time of year – in this case spring) and find the plants illustrated on the photocopiable sheet. From these observations, or from pictures, the children can use colour to improve the drawings and label the three parts of the plant. They should write where they found the plants in the space provided on the sheet. Point out to the children that the tree's trunk is considered a stem.

Differentiation: Enlarge the sheet for the less able children. Make some labels for them to stick in the right places.

Extension: This sheet must be part of ongoing observations of plants. Get the children to observe the growth of plants from seeds (for example, cress, beans, peas, sunflower and marrow). Make a classroom chart listing the places where the children found the plants. *What other plants can be found in the immediate area?* Check the cracks in the paving stones, on the lawn and so on.

Growing food (page 92)

Objective: To understand that some plants provide food for humans.

What to do: *Which of these plants do humans eat?* Children connect the plants that we eat to the plate by drawing lines. Make sure they understand that some plants are poisonous.

Differentiation: Play a 'point and name' game with the children. *What is this? Do we eat it?* Less able children will need a great deal of discussion of this sort. Ask the question *Have you ever seen this on a plate?*

Extension: Make sure that the children understand that we don't eat everything that grows. Ask them to list things in the fridge/cupboard/larder/lunch box that were once growing plants. (A possible homework task.)

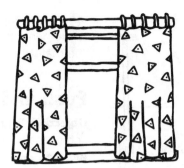

Material mad (page 93)

Objective: To understand that objects are made from materials and that different materials have different uses.

What to do: Have fun with the picture. *What's wrong?* Make it clear that all the clothes are made from materials, but not necessarily the best material for the job. Discuss this with the children. Ask them to suggest which materials they should be made from. They can fill the blanks with these words. Use a class dictionary of materials or a wordbank to support the children.

Differentiation: Less able children could re-draw the girl, this time wearing clothes made from sensible materials.

Extension: Make classroom collections of materials, for example wooden objects or different types of paper and card. Discuss what they can be used for: *Which type of paper would be best for using as a tissue; writing a letter on; or wrapping a present?*

How does it look and feel?

(page 94)

Objective: To use the appropriate vocabulary to describe materials.

What to do: Clearly the children must first identify the objects. You might build up a class book of describing words (rough, smooth, shiny, dull and so on). Children list the materials on the chart provided, and write words that describe them. The pictures are of common objects – have them on hand for the children to look at and handle. (Safety note: glass bottles and so on should generally be avoided in the classroom with young children, although common at home. Use under strictly controlled conditions. Glass can usually be touched in the form of windowpanes.) In a group, or with the whole class, get the children to describe the properties of the objects appropriately.

Differentiation: Science and experience are most

important here, so if the writing proves to be a major obstacle, get the children to tell their answers to an adult who can write for them. Alternatively, they could record the answers on the computer. Set up a wordbank on the computer for the children to choose words from.

Extension: Ask the children to make a short list of objects/materials in the classroom, or at home, that have certain defined properties, for example rough, bendy, or dull.

What's it like? (page 95)

Objective: To use appropriate vocabulary to describe materials.

What to do: Children choose an object (from the class 'tinkering table' perhaps) and draw it in the space provided on the sheet. They should then write as many words as they can that describe their object on the lines radiating outwards. The words at the bottom of the page will help them or they can think of their own.

Differentiation: Less able children could work in a group under adult supervision. The adult could write down the words for them.

Extension: Children can explore materials to see which are magnetic and which are not. This could be done via a 'tinkering table' in the classroom. This should be a hands-on activity – any writing should be of secondary importance.

What could you use to...? (page 96)

Objective: To think about which materials are suitable for particular purposes.

What to do: Choosing from the list at the bottom of the sheet, the children write down the names of the materials that would be most useful in making the items shown. Allow more than one material to be recorded where this is clearly appropriate (for example, a saw – wood/plastic for the handle, metal for the blade).

Differentiation: With less able children, lots of talk and handling of materials is essential. Seek to establish what it is about a material that makes it suitable – they might know from experience that paper is good for wrapping a parcel, but why? (Thin, light, flexible and so on.)

Extension: Ask the children to establish criteria for selecting the material to do a particular job such as holding water, a toy for a baby, a dinner plate, a box for lunches, a window for a doll's house and so on.

Light and dark (page 97)

Objective: To learn that there are many sources of light.

What to do: The children need to look closely at the top picture. This may work best in a small group rather than individually. When they have seen the light, children colour in the various sources for the night-time scene. Discuss the second picture with them and let them colour in the sun if they wish.

Differentiation: Some children may not cope very well with using colour on such a small picture. You could enlarge it, or get the children to circle the sources of light rather than using colour.

Extension: Sources of light show up best at night-time. Explore this idea. Children could learn about Christmas, Divali, Guy Fawkes Night and so on, where lights and fireworks are used as part of the celebration. Get the children to paint 'light' and 'dark' pictures.

Ways to move (page 98)

Objective: To observe and describe different ways of moving.

What to do: Pictures tell only part of the story and the children should watch and think about movement in PE lessons or in the playground before completing the photocopiable sheet. Show them the sheet and ask: *How are these children moving? Can you find a word at the bottom of the page that describes what they are doing?* Children write the word by the picture.

Differentiation: Read the words at the bottom of the page to those children that require this help. Talk through the pictures to make sure that they have the correct vocabulary to describe what is happening. If necessary (and practical), get children to demonstrate the action. Children need not write the words themselves, if this is a problem. They can say or stick the words, or dictate them to an adult to write down.

Extension: This bit of science moves neatly into a PE lesson so the best follow-up is to use the descriptive language and get the children to match their movements to your words, for example *move across the mat with a jump and a twist.*

Push and pull (page 99)

Objective: To begin to know that forces such as pushes and pulls can move objects.

What to do: Discuss how the things in the pictures are being made to move. Ask: *Who or what is pushing and pulling? How do you know?* Get the children to use the word *because*. When they can adequately describe what is happening, they write *push* or *pull* in the blank labels that are drawn as directional arrows.

Differentiation: Most children should manage this photocopiable sheet, some may need more oral prompts and encouragement to keep them on task. This requires an adult in support.

Extension: Ask the children to find out about toys that need to be moved by pushing or pulling. They could focus on classroom toys, or do this as a homework exercise. They could make lists, demonstrate the toys, or simply talk about them.

Pushing and pulling at home (page 100)

Objective: To identify things in the home which are moved by pushing or pulling.

What to do: Although there are lots of words on this sheet, it is still essentially about observation of movement. Make sure that the children recognise and know the words at the top of the sheet (*pulling/ pushing*). Children should complete the sheet by writing the correct words on the lines.

Differentiation: Allow more able children to complete the sheet themselves. Many children will need to have the sentences read to them so that they can then fill in the gaps. Note that more observant children may point out that you can close doors by pulling as well as pushing – it depends on which side of the door you are on. Praise children who note things like this. (In the drawing there can only be one answer.)

Extension: Children need to recognise that there are hazards in moving (or stopping) some objects. Get them to look at the pictures on the sheet and to spot the dangers involved in pushing and pulling (fingers trapped in doors/drawers and so on). For additional work at home, they might see what dangers of this sort they could find in, say, their own bedroom.

What makes it move? (page 101)

Objectives: To ask questions about what is causing movement and to understand that it is not only ourselves that cause things to move.

What to do: The children read the sentences on the photocopiable sheet and complete them using the words at the top of the page – *wind* or *water*. The toy windmill has not been supplied with a sentence. Challenge the children to describe what is causing it to move, they can then write their own sentence about it. The answers are: wind; water; wind; wind; breath.

Differentiation: Support less able children with the reading and talk through the pictures with them in order to tease out the causes of movement.

Extension: Collect questions from children about what makes things move. *What makes a car move? What makes smoke move?* Compile a classroom chart of the questions and illustrate it. There is no need to get into detailed scientific explanations – asking the questions and recognising that something causes movement is important in itself. Give simple explanations.

Watch out! Because... (page 102)

Objective: To recognise hazards and risks to themselves from moving objects.

What to do: The labels should be cut out first. On this sheet, the children look for hazards caused by moving objects. When they spot one they stick a label on the hazard. They should present the completed sheet to an adult and describe why there is a danger. Encourage the children to use the word *because*. For example, *Don't walk behind a swing because it may swing back and hit you.*

Differentiation: The quality of the answers will differentiate between more able and less able children. Those who have difficulty with this exercise will find support by working in a group. Enlarge the sheet and do it as a group activity with adult support if needed.

Extension: It would be worth extending this activity into a discussion of road safety. Stopping a moving car with our bodies is dangerous. Get a suitable road safety video to show to the children to stimulate discussion. Learn the Green Cross Code.

Barmy band (page 103)

Objective: To describe the way in which sounds are made by musical instruments.

What to do: Ask the children: *Are these animals playing their instruments correctly?* Talk about what they can see. *How is the mouse playing the recorder? Is this the correct way to play a recorder?* Challenge them to say how the instruments really should be played to make the sounds. Can they spot the ones being played correctly? (Tuba, violin, double bass.) Ask them to circle these. Then ask them to complete the sentences using the words from the box.

Differentiation: All children need to have experience of listening to and watching instruments being played. They should try playing as many instruments as is possible. Give less able children a chance to blow a recorder, pluck a guitar, beat a drum, shake a tambourine and so on. For those children that need support to complete this sheet, provide demonstration, where possible, and talk through the process of producing a sound from an instrument. Do this in a group.

Extension: Add to the list of instruments and challenge the children to say how to make sounds with them. The terms *shake, pluck, bang, blow* and *hit* broadly cover them all. Ask them to group the instruments according to these categories. Make a chart of the results.

Loud or quiet? (page 104)

Objective: To learn that there are many ways of describing sounds.

What to do: Tell the children to study the pictures on the sheet and think of words to describe the sounds. They may use the words at the bottom of the page but encourage them to use words of their own.

Differentiation: Less able children can stick to the words provided at the bottom of the page. Elicit a wider range of words from more able children.

Extension: Play recordings of (or make) sounds for the children to describe in their own words. Can they guess what they are? For example, a running tap, a ticking clock, someone switching on a light, a car driving down the road, and so on. Ask the children to list the sounds they can hear when standing in the kitchen at home. Can they sort them into loud and soft sounds?

Sounds I can make (page 105)

Objective: To begin to explore the sounds we ourselves can make.

What to do: Ask the children to make all of the sounds that are illustrated. When they have reproduced them correctly they should choose the appropriate word from those provided and write them into the spaces under the pictures.

Differentiation: Instead of writing the words, less able children could cut them out and stick them into the spaces. Read the words to less able children but only after they have worked out what the sounds are.

Extension: *Are there any other sounds that we can make?* (Treat the noise and chaos as a bit of light relief.) You can make a 'mouth' orchestra just using mouth sounds – perhaps best left until the children have more control! Get the children to join in 'The Happy Song', by Flanders and Swann (available on *At the Drop of a Hat,* (EMI)), making the 'mouth' noises.

Body parts

Match the words from the bottom of the page to the parts of the body.

elbow	ear	nose	mouth	knee
arm	leg	head	eye	neck

Five senses

Fill in the blanks with the correct word from the right.

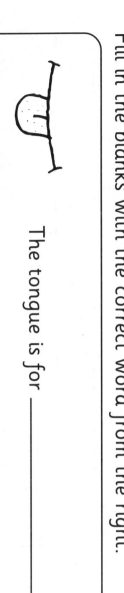

The tongue is for _____.

The eyes are for _____.

The hands are for _____.

The nose is for _____.

The ears are for _____.

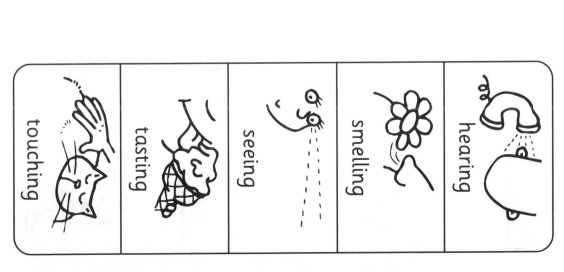

touching

tasting

seeing

smelling

hearing

Am I an animal?

Sort the pictures into the correct box.

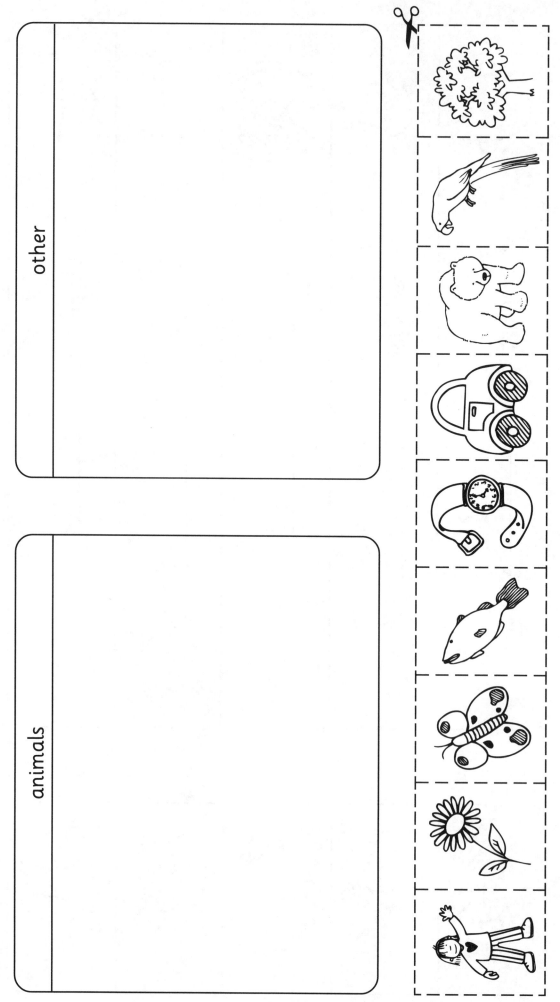

animals

other

Adults and young

Match the young animal to the adult.

Alive and not alive

Sort the pictures into the correct box.

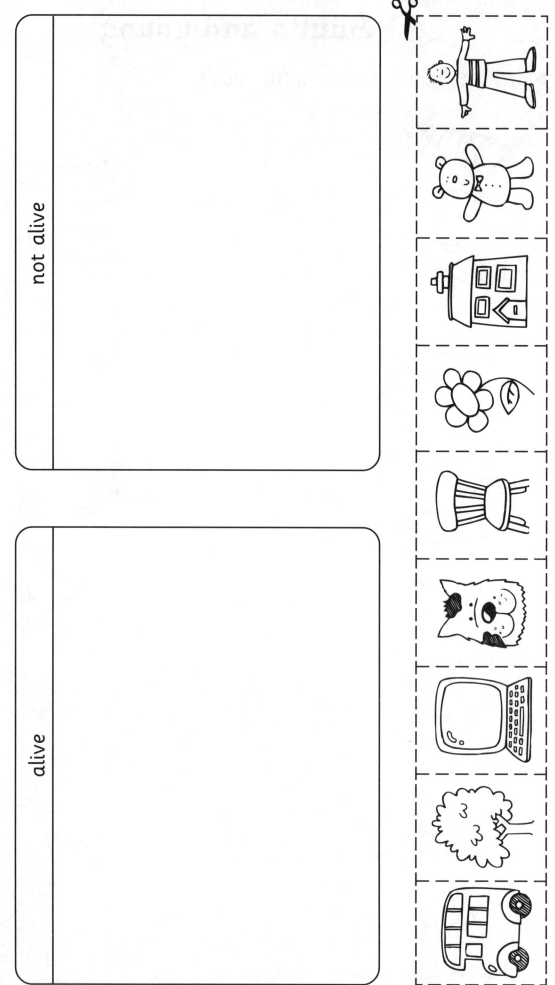

alive

not alive

Plants around school

- Can you find these plants?
- Colour in and label these parts: stem flower leaf

crocus

daffodil

tulip

tree

- Write where you found them in the boxes.

Growing food

We eat some plants. Which might end up on your plate?
Draw a line from the plants we can eat to the plate.

Material mad

Is this sensible? What do you think these clothes **should** be made from? Write your answers in the boxes.

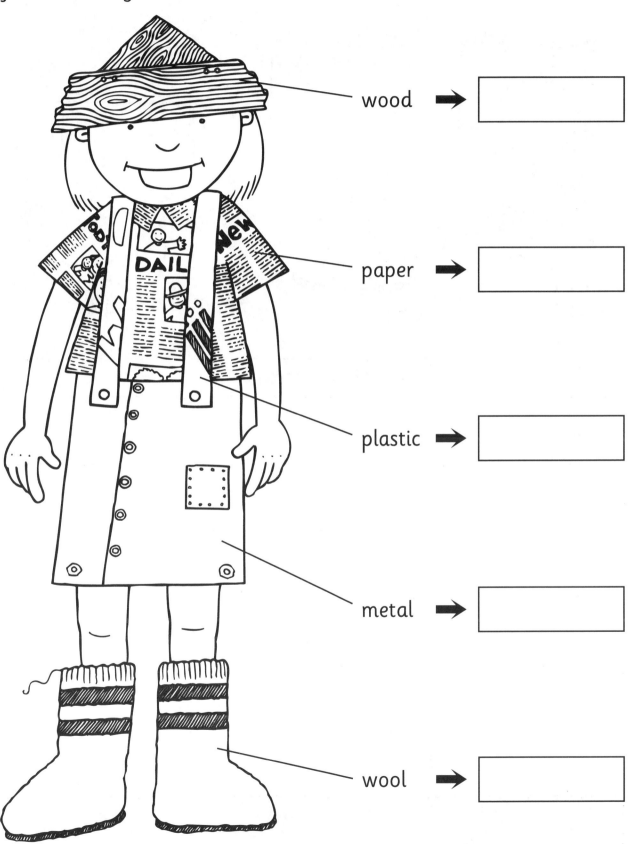

wood ➡

paper ➡

plastic ➡

metal ➡

wool ➡

How does it look and feel?

- Write each material in the chart below.
- What words can you think of to describe them?

fabric

plastic

wood

brick

clay

sand

glass

	describing words
fabric	

What's it like?

- Choose an object and draw it in the circle.
- Write describing words on the lines.

shiny   smooth   rough   hard   soft   strong

dull   bendy   magnetic   waterproof   transparent

What could you use to...?

Write down materials that you could use...

to wrap a parcel

_____

to make a shirt

_____

to hold a drink

_____

to build a hutch

_____

to make a saw

_____

Materials (plastic) (glass) (string) (cotton)
(metal) (wood) (paper) (clay) (fabric)

Light and dark

● Use colours to show where the light comes from at night.

● Where does the light come from in the daytime?

Ways to move

How are these children moving?

(jumping) (swinging) (sliding)

(crawling) (climbing) (twisting)

Push and pull

Write **push** or **pull** in the arrows.

Pushing and pulling at home

When do you push and pull at home?
Write the correct word in the spaces.

(pulling)   (pushing)

I shut the door by _____.

I open the door by _____.

I shut the drawer by _____.

I open the drawer by _____.

I switch on the light by _____.

I open the window by _____.

What makes it move?

Write the correct word in the spaces.   wind   water

The _____

makes the branches move.

The _____

makes the wheel turn.

The _____

makes the sailing boat move.

The _____

makes the washing move.

_____

_____

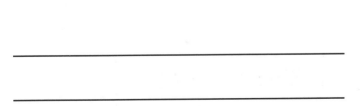

Watch out! Because...

Stick labels on the dangers in this picture. Say why.

Be careful! Be careful! Be careful!

Be careful! Be careful!

Barmy band

● What's wrong with this band?

● Choose the correct word from the box to complete the
sentences. We should...

_____ a triangle.

_____ a drum.

_____ a trumpet.

_____ a tambourine.

_____ a guitar.

pluck

hit

shake

bang

blow

Loud or quiet?

● Describe the sounds.

| loud | soft | quiet | high | low |

● Can you think of any more words?

Sounds I can make

What sounds are these children making?

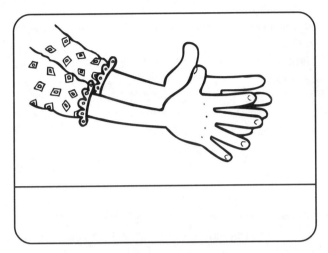

| crying | stamping | singing |
| clapping | whistling | whispering |

HISTORY

If one thinks purely in terms of historical periods and significant events, the content of the history curriculum seems to be barely defined at all for Year 1 children. Nevertheless, the content is there, it is just that the teacher is free to choose the particular way in which the general knowledge, skills and understanding will be taught. Clearly these photocopiables could not cover all the choices and possibilities, so we have focused on the general areas identified in the QCA Scheme of Work for Year 1, especially the first two units in the scheme. These deal with toys and homes.

Of course these topics are merely pegs on which to hang important historical learning. Although children of this age are likely to do very little history, they are beginning to be aware of the passing of time, and foundations are being laid for future learning. The photocopiable worksheets in this chapter therefore have a fairly narrow focus. They will particularly support teaching that is concerned with (a) historical enquiry (to ask and answer questions about the past), and (b) knowledge and understanding of people and changes in the past (identifying differences between ways of life then and now).

There are several excellent books that deal with infant historical projects. There are many on recent and oral history and guidance on teaching Victorian projects is particularly widely available. (See for example *The Victorian Schoolday*, A Teacher's Manual, W Frankum and J Lawrie obtainable from Katesgrove Schoolroom, Dorothy Street, Reading.)

What are they playing at?

(page 109)

Objectives: To describe old and new toys and to begin to distinguish between them.

What to do: On this sheet, the children have to connect each child and toy to the right box by drawing a line. This sheet is essentially a discussion activity. The process of matching the right child and toy to the right box is meaningless unless the children have the opportunity to interrogate the evidence. Get the children (or preferably a small group) to describe what they see in the pictures. *What is happening? Could this be happening now? How can you tell?* And so on.

Differentiation: You can reduce the problem for less able children by cutting out the pictures for them to physically sort into piles – then and now. This will help to reduce the confusion of being faced with many choices but the problem is still the same and oral support will be required. Look for clues. Listen to the children. Give them time.

Extension: The objects are not, in themselves, that important, but the people, and the way they lived, are. Ask the children to talk about how the toys were actually used. *Why did children long ago not play with computer games? Who could you ask about old toys? Who might know?* If possible, get each child to bring a toy from home (old or new) and talk about how it is played with.

Who do these belong to? (page 110)

Objectives: To learn how to decide whether an object is old or new and to begin to describe them.

What to do: This is a variation on the last sheet. In this instance, the children need to look more closely at the toys themselves. First they have to decide which child is *then* and which is *now* before they allocate the correct toys to the children, by drawing a line. Note that they could place the yo-yo in either category although a wooden version would have been used in the past. Look more closely at the toys with the children and ask: *How are they different? How are they the same? How can we tell which is which?*

Differentiation: Because the answers are not necessarily clear cut (a modern child might have access to and play with a 1950s Dinky Toy!), it is very important that the children are involved in discussing the activity. Encourage all children, but particularly those who find this exercise difficult, to 'think out loud'.

Extension: Ideally, the children should experience the real thing. Set up a classroom display of toys, old and new, taking all the usual safety and security precautions. Perhaps the local museum service will help with loan material. Ask the children, as homework, to talk to an adult (for example, granddad) about a toy that they played with when young. The children should then report back to the class about what they have found out. Alternatively, arrange for an elderly visitor to talk to the class.

Old and new (page 111)

Objective: To identify the characteristic features of old and new objects.

What to do: The children will need to draw a line to match the descriptive words at the bottom of the sheet to the most appropriate toy. Either as a group exercise or by providing individual support, talk the children through the characteristics of the objects. First of all get them to decide which objects are new and which are old and then encourage them to try and think of their own adjectives to describe the toys.

Differentiation: You can simplify the task by cutting out the pictures and then placing the old and new objects side by side. Cut out the words and allow the children to place them correctly.

Extension: The object of the exercise is to elicit descriptive words from the children so that they begin to define the distinction between old and new. Ask them to find words of their own to add to the 'old' and the 'new' lists.

Where people live (page 112)

Objectives: To understand that people live in different sorts of homes and to talk about homes using appropriate vocabulary.

What to do: Ask the children to identify the picture that is most like the house that they live in. They could do this by colouring, or by marking a border around the picture. *In what way does it look like your home?* Ask them to describe common features such as the same sort of windows, built of brick, semi-detached, and so on. The children can use the blank square to draw a small sketch of their home.

Differentiation: Once again, discussion is the important feature of using this sheet and the less able children will need an adult to tease the words and descriptions out of them. Some children may find it easier to describe their home. If you have use of a digital or other instant camera, photographs can be used to help. The more able children should be asked to use the correct words to describe at least one of the pictures (semi-detached, high-rise flat, mobile home, farmhouse and so on).

Extension: A classroom display of pictures (taken on a digital camera and printed on the computer) of all the children's homes would make a splendid starting

point for a discussion of the features of different homes. Be aware that although children will not be sensitive on this issue, some parents might be, and pictures should only be taken and displayed with parental co-operation.

A house from the past (page 113)

Objective: To identify the key features of a home built a long time ago.

What to do: Children need to identify and label the features of this typical large and elaborate late-19th-century house. It has a semi-basement (by the end of the century, people realised basements were damp and unhealthy and semi-basements – down about three feet – became common from the 1860s onwards). The Victorians introduced bay windows and gradually phased out basements. The steps were a bridge over the 'area', a small yard below street level. You will need to talk about the features of houses before the children attempt the sheet. The object is to get children to look closely at the features of this house and think about how it is different from their own houses. Ask them what they think the house is made from (bricks). Can they work out how the windows open? (The windows are sash windows and are opened by sliding up or down.)

Differentiation: Some children may have a problem with the vocabulary so make sure that you support the less confident children by providing lots of suitable words. Make a display of house pictures. Get the children used to using the correct descriptive words. Provide a wordbank of suitable words. Individual discussion with an adult would be helpful.

Extension: Get each child to write down the word labels given and to draw a picture of the part described. Ask the children to write (or say) three descriptive sentences about the house that they live in, focusing on its external physical features. Give them questions to get them started such as *What is it made of? How many storeys does it have? How do the windows open?*

Household objects from a long time ago (page 114)

Objectives: To recognise household objects from a long time ago and to make inferences from them about aspects of home life in the past.

What to do: There are two aspects to this sheet. First, the children need to name the objects. They can do this by either drawing a line to the correct label at the bottom of the sheet or by writing (or cutting and sticking) the name on the line provided. They should then complete a line of writing for each object about what it is used for. This should be preceded by class discussion about the drawings. Ideally similar objects should be available in a class display on a 'tinkering table'. Check with the museum service, members of staff, or grandparents.

Differentiation: For the less able children this should become purely an oral exercise. An adult could write down the children's answers and then the children might copy these. It is the thinking and the talking that is important.

Extension: Ask the children to see if their parents or grandparents have a household object that is very old. If it is neither valuable nor fragile, ask if they can bring it to school to show and talk about.

Home life (page 115)

Objectives: To recognise household objects from a long time ago and to make inferences from them about aspects of home life in the past.

What to do: Children may not have seen any of these objects, so you must engage them in detective work. First encourage them to describe what they see. *What does it look like? What is it made of? How big is it? How does it work? What do you think it does?* Then ask them to name the objects using the labels at the bottom of the page.

Differentiation: Some children will make good guesses as to what the objects are without the prompts of the labels. Less able children will need the prompts and an adult should read out the words to them at the appropriate time.

Extension: Having sorted out what these objects were used for, the next question to ask is: *Why were they needed? Why a mangle? Why a hand-powered sewing machine? Why a paraffin lamp? Why a piano?* The last question could spark an interesting discussion, as some children will have a piano at home. *But was it different then?* Ask the children to make a list of what objects we use instead today. (For example, washing machine, electric lamp.) At some point children should visit an appropriate hands-on small museum where they can see and handle these and similar objects.

What has changed? (page 116)

Objective: To make inferences about life a long time ago and to spot changes between now and then.

What to do: The two *then* illustrations are early 20th century. The children should not find it too difficult to match the people to the vehicles. Let them cut the pictures out and mount them in a book. More able children could write a sentence about each picture. Get the children to talk about the differences they can see between the two vehicles. How can they tell which vehicle belongs to which couple?

Differentiation: Less able children could circle any differences they can spot between vehicles (and between people) and talk about these differences. More able children may be able to write about the differences.

Extension: Although you may ask more able children to write about the differences that they see, there are other ways of communicating knowledge – through talk, play, drama and so on. Ask the children to imagine what it must have been like to travel on the upstairs of an old open-topped omnibus. *How did you pay your fare? What has changed since then? Why do modern buses have doors on them?*

Put these toys into the correct boxes. How can you tell where to put them?

What are they playing at?

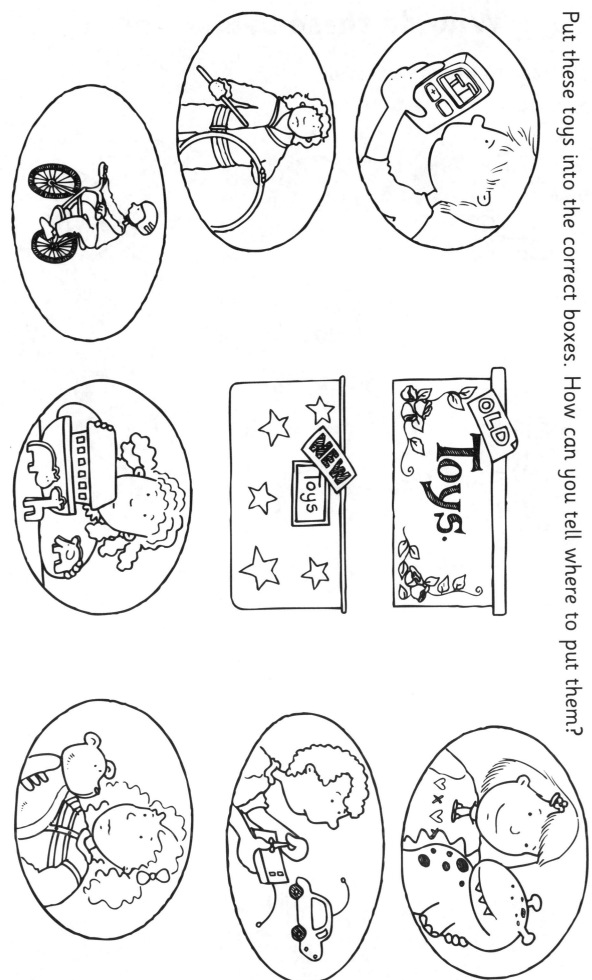

Who do these belong to?

Join the toys to the correct child.

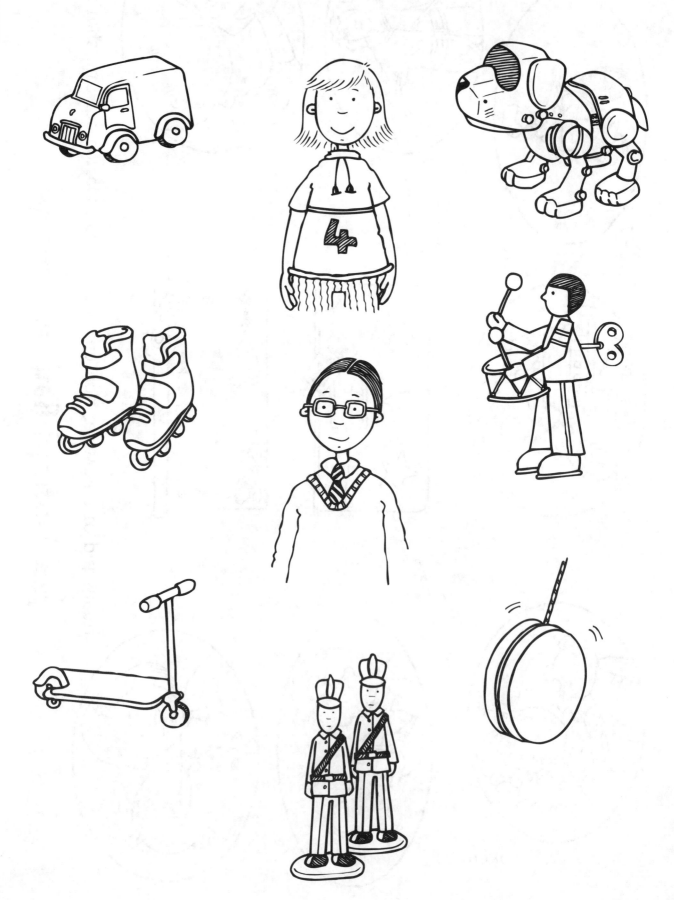

Old and new

Describe these toys.

clean   shiny   metal   plastic   worn

dirty   broken   modern   old   used   new

Where people live

- Which home is most like yours?
- Draw your home in the blank square.

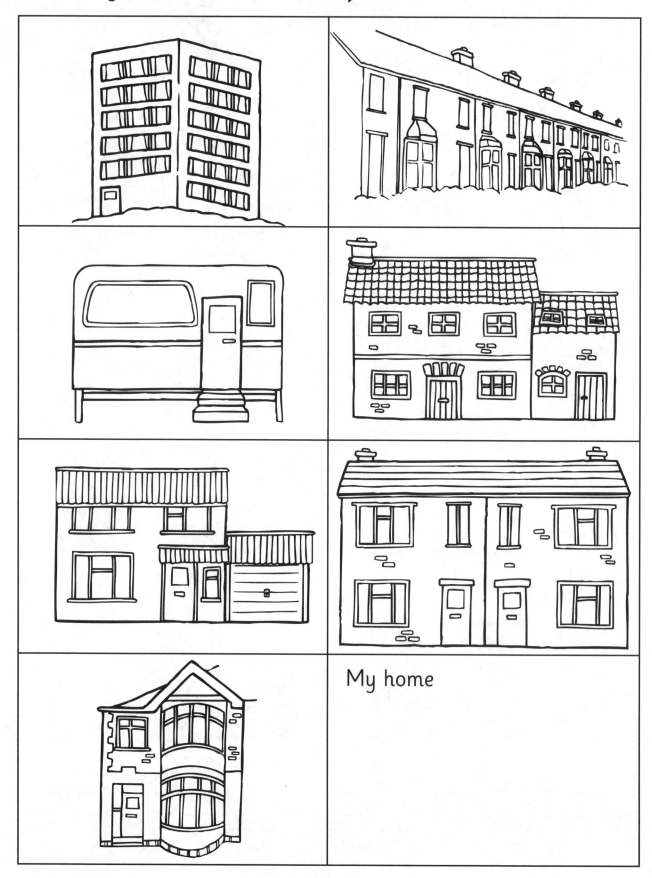

My home

A house from the past

- Match the words to the correct part of the house.
- How is this house different from your home?

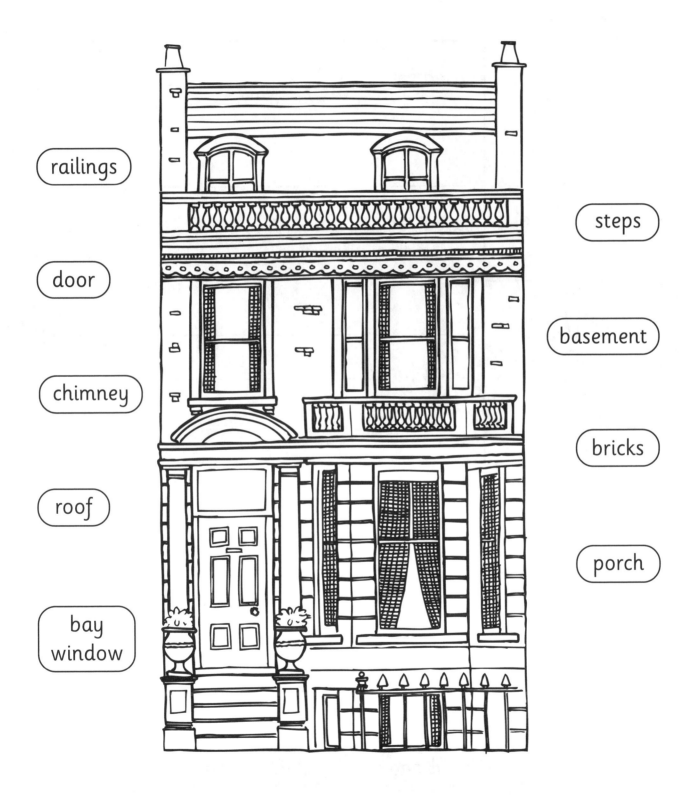

railings

door

chimney

roof

bay window

steps

basement

bricks

porch

Household objects from a long time ago

● What are these objects?
● What were they used for?

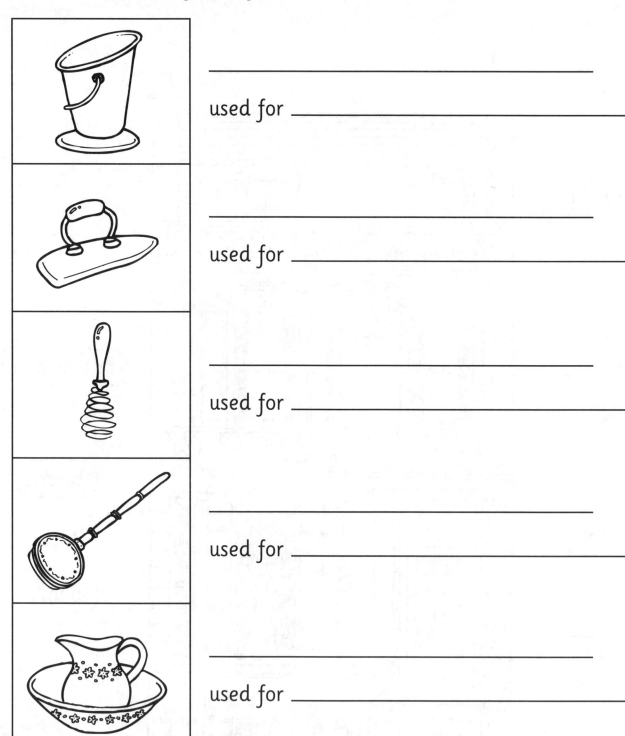

_____

used for _____

_____

used for _____

_____

used for _____

_____

used for _____

_____

used for _____

(Bowl and jug) (Coal scuttle)

(Egg whisk) (Flat iron) (Warming-pan)

Home life

- Describe these objects.
- What are they called?

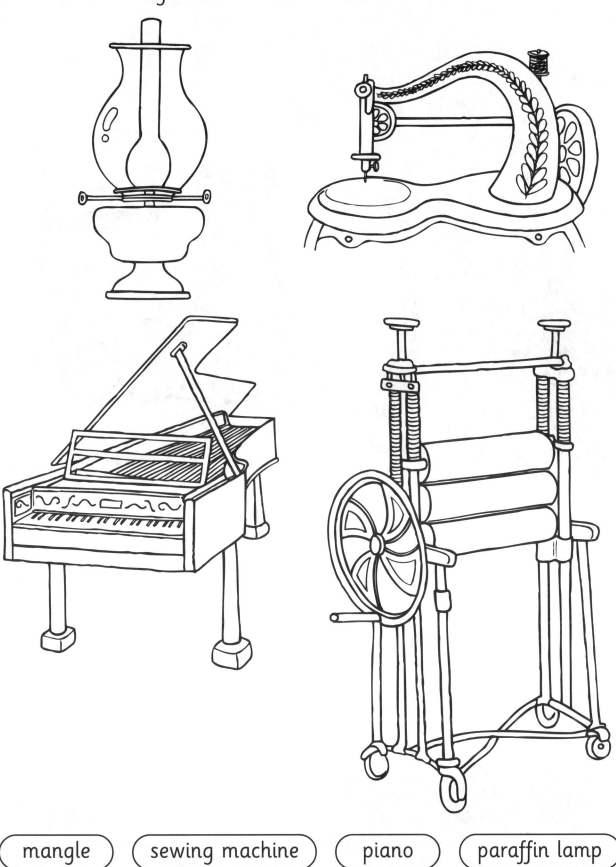

(mangle) (sewing machine) (piano) (paraffin lamp)

What has changed?

- Which bus would these people travel on?
- Talk about the changes you can see.

GEOGRAPHY

There is a core of what the National Curriculum calls 'geographical enquiry and skills' that runs throughout the geography curriculum for Key Stage 1. These 'skills' are in fact very general skills that are exercised in a geographical context, such as asking questions, observing and recording, expressing views and communicating in different ways. These worksheets are primarily concerned with developing and practising these skills. As for content, the Breadth of Study specified in the National Curriculum makes it clear that children are going to start their geographical studies at a local level. Across this key stage, children will study two localities (a) the locality of the school, and (b) a contrasting locality in the United Kingdom or overseas. Year 1 focuses on (a).

In the QCA Scheme of Work, two units are allocated to Year 1. One that deals with the local area ('Around our school') as a long study, and one that deals with the local area in an issue-based way as a short unit ('How can we make our local area safer?'). The following worksheets will support work for these units. It cannot be stressed too often that although worksheets support learning, they do not ensure that it takes place. It is certain that if the children are to develop any true understanding of the locality then they must get outside the classroom and undertake fieldwork. Firsthand experience is essential, particularly when the QCA scheme specifies *places, themes and skills*. Children should walk around the area and experience it. They must practise and develop their skills in the context of fieldwork. When they have experienced and know the environment under scrutiny they should express views on environmental change. The following worksheets will work best in this context.

Going to school (page 120)

Objectives: To carry out a survey of how children travel to school and to represent this on a simple graph.

What to do: Get the children to work in groups of six or more. Cut out the 'stickers' for those children that need support before carrying out the survey. The children in each group should ask each other how they travel to school and then stick the appropriate descriptive picture on the chart. Each child completes their own graph. You will need to show those children who have not constructed a graph of any sort before how to do this. Note that one column is blank. Children can use this as they wish or leave it as 'other'. Follow up the activity by getting the children to draw some conclusions from the graph, such as: *Which is the most popular method of travel to school? Which is the least popular? How can you tell? Why?* They can

communicate their conclusions orally or in writing.

Differentiation: More able children might do this sheet unaided and you could allocate them a larger group of children to survey (duplicate more stickers). Less confident children could work on their graphs in a group. Photo-enlarge the sheet to make the exercise less fiddly.

Extension: Children could make graphs recording a larger sample or you may get them to produce their graphs on the computer as a follow-up activity.

On the way to school (page 121)

Objective: To recognise some of the physical features in their locality.

What to do: Talk to the children about their journey to school. Get them to complete the blanks on the sheet by drawing small sketches of their house and their school. Tell them to take a pretend walk down the path. Every time they pass an object they must say whether or not they would pass one on their real route to school. They should tick what they would pass.

Differentiation: Can children identify the buildings and street furniture on the sheet? Make sure that this is the case. Encourage less able children to describe each drawing in their own words by asking *What do you think this is? Have you seen one before? Is there one on your way to school?* For all children, but particularly for those who find it hard to recall the route, there is no substitute for walking the ground. Where possible they should carry this out with a sheet and clipboard.

Extension: Ask the children to add three or more things that they pass on the way to school not already shown on the sheet. (A possible homework exercise.) Depending on the children's ability, they may attempt a picture map of their route to school.

Where I live (page 122)

Objective: To understand that we all have a personal address and what this address means.

What to do: Ask the children: *What is an address?* Discuss each line of the school address with the children and make sure they understand it. *What does each line mean? What is it for? How does it help to get a letter to its destination?* Tackling the sheet should be fairly straightforward. The children should link the pictures of nursery rhyme characters by a line to the letter that they are intended to receive. Provide a real envelope for children to address to themselves (or their parents) at their own address.

Differentiation: Children should be able to tease out the clues and recognise the 'surname' word in the address from their experience of nursery rhymes. However, support should be given to those children whose reading is not up to the exercise. This exercise is about lines of an address, not about reading obscure place names.

Extension: Letter writing is not so common today. Ask the children to write a letter to someone in their house or in their class. They must address it correctly. Walk with the class to the post-box and post the letters (don't use the school mailing system!). They should see how the system works and that it does work. Organise it so that every child (or household) will receive a letter through the letterbox. Ask them to bring it to school. Discuss what has happened to the letters. Addresses can also be displayed on a large-scale wall map of the locality.

Nice and nasty (page 123)

Objective: To begin to use a range of words and pictures to describe the quality of the environment.

What to do: Start by talking to the children about what makes a place 'nice' or 'nasty'. The sheet should be self-explanatory. What it cannot show is the range of descriptive vocabulary that might be employed when discussing why places are nice and nasty. When the children have finished their pictures, encourage them to say why they think that their chosen part of the locality is 'nice'. What words can they use to describe it? Assist them to express and, if possible, to record their views.

Differentiation: Most children should manage this photocopiable as it will be differentiated by outcome. More able children will employ a richer vocabulary and express and record their views more skilfully.

Extension: Challenge children to make a list of the 'nice' parts of their environment (alternatively, of course, the 'nasty' parts.) With the help of an adult, children could take photographs. How do they think the nasty parts could be improved?

What happens here? (page 124)

Objective: To identify some of the uses of land and buildings in their locality.

What to do: This is a cloze-procedure sheet with picture clues. The children select the appropriate word from the bottom of the sheet and complete the sentences, either by writing or cutting and pasting the labels. The blank picture box is provided for the children's pictures and they complete the sentence as appropriate, for example *My mum works here.*

Differentiation: It is critical that the children can identify the buildings and know what goes on in them. Discuss with the class what each picture represents. Read the incomplete sentences and words at the bottom of the sheet out loud to less able children.

Extension: The best extension to this worksheet is a visit to one of the buildings. In groups of an effective size, visit the supermarket or some other place of work. Carry out a survey of a main street. Photograph all the places that people work in and discuss what happens there. *What does Daddy or Mummy do?* type of investigations are fruitful but can be insensitive (unemployment). Think before embarking on them. As a homework task you could ask the children to make a list of all the places that people work in on their route to school.

Leisure tally (page 125)

Objectives: To understand about leisure and its need for special facilities and to learn how to tally.

What to do: This is primarily about leisure but is also an exercise in tallying. Teach those children who are able how to use this technique. The sheet leaves it open for you to define the target group; it could be a family, or the staff of the school. A reasonable size sample is needed – at least ten.

Differentiation: Less able children can record a mark for each person and dispense with tallying in groups of five. If necessary, use a very small sample and allow them to colour a square for each answer recorded.

Extension: Adapt the chart to allow for a larger sample – the results are then more interesting and can form the basis for useful discussion. For a homework assignment, ask the children to list all the special leisure facilities in their nearest town (sports centres, swimming pools, golf ranges, bingo halls and so on).

Making safe (page 126)

Objective: To understand that places can be made safer or better.

What to do: From the array of pictures on the photocopiable, children choose things that would positively improve the quality of their street. They can cut out the pictures and stick them in the space provided, or link them to the space with a line. They are limited to choosing four things only (they might begin to understand that you can never do everything!). Follow up with a whole-class discussion of their choices: *What else might make your street safer?*

Differentiation: Encourage more able children to name the objects in the pictures (thus extending their vocabulary to describe the environment). Less able children should connect using arrows to avoid messy sticking, and may need adult support to make appropriate choices.

Extension: A key objective is to get the children to express views about making their own area safer. Ask them to list the most dangerous places in their area. *Why are they dangerous?* This might link to a number of issues – quality of life, road safety, stranger danger and so on.

Traffic count (page 127)

Objectives: To ask questions about roads and traffic, and to collect data and display it in a graphical form.

What to do: This is clearly not a sheet for the children to attempt unsupervised. They should first record the vehicle by a dot in the square. Back in the classroom they can turn it into a coloured block chart. Make sure you time-limit the survey. Know the road that you are surveying and adjust the time accordingly. It should be quite short – even five minutes may be too long for some busy roads. If undertaken by a whole class, assign groups a set period and then co-ordinate the results into a large chart.

Differentiation: The task is made easier if a group undertakes it, then each child is allocated one type of vehicle only to survey. You may also need to limit the survey to traffic travelling in one direction only.

Extension: From a simple survey like this it is easy to expand into something bigger. Children might carry out a survey of traffic from their bedroom window ten minutes before they go to bed (or similar).

Going to school

- Ask six friends how they travel to school.
- Cut out stickers for them and stick them in the right column.

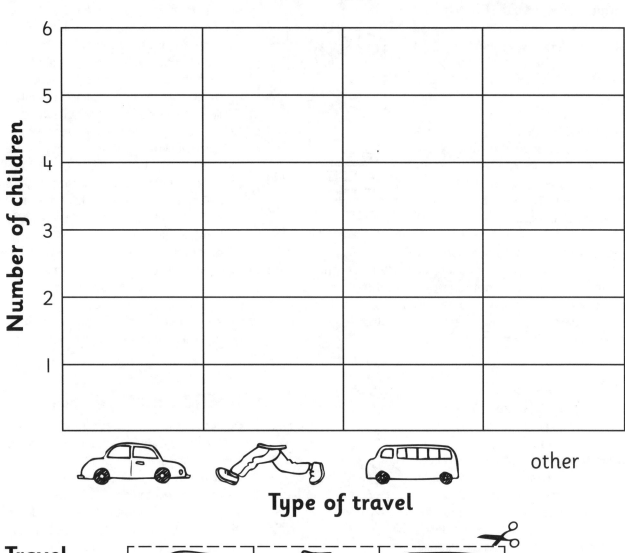

Number of children

Type of travel

other

Travel stickers

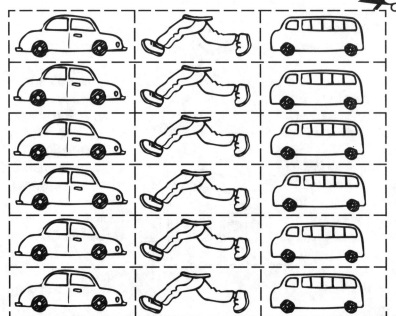

On the way to school

- Fill in the missing pictures.
- Then tick what you pass on the way to school.

my house

post-box

litter bin

Post Office

traffic lights

church

seat

sign post

PUBLIC FOOTPATH

my school

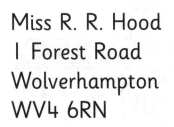

Where I live

Who lives where? Match the characters to their addresses.

Miss B. Peep
14 Sheep Close
Crook
Durham
DU7 6RN

Miss R. R. Hood
1 Forest Road
Wolverhampton
WV4 6RN

Miss L. Muffett
32 Tuffet Street
Weybridge
GU7 2BB

Mr H. Dumpty
5 Brick Drive
Wallsend
NE4 3GG

Nice and nasty

● Colour the places that you think are nice. Why are they nice?

● Draw a nice part of your town. Why is it nice?

What happens here?

Finish the sentences.

	Cars are _____ here.
	People _____ here.
	_____ work here.
	Things are _____ here.
	There are many _____ in these offices.
	_____ are kept here.
	My _____ works here.

made	buy things	mended
Doctors and nurses	computers	Fire engines

Leisure tally

● Ask some adults about their favourite leisure activities. Put a mark (I) for each person's favourite.

● Which is the most popular? Colour the activities that need a special building.

	⊦⊦⊦⊦	⊦⊦⊦⊦	⊦⊦⊦⊦	Total

Making safe

● Choose four things from below that might make your street safe and more pleasant to live in. Can you say why?

● Cut them out and stick them in this space.

Traffic count

Stand in a safe place with an adult. Colour one space for each vehicle you see.

	1	2	3	4	5	6	7	8	9	10	11	12	13	14	15
other															

DESIGN AND TECHNOLOGY

More than anything, design and technology in the National Curriculum is concerned with developing ideas – planning, making products, and evaluating them. Three ways are suggested in which this can be done: (1) investigating familiar products; (2) practical tasks (for developing skills and techniques); and (3) designing and making products. Practical experience is essential to all work at Key Stage 1, but particularly in design and technology. This is time consuming, so it is worth noting that the QCA Scheme of Work for Year 1 is allocated up to 39 hours, which compares with science (49 hours) and history (16 hours).

In the kingdom of 'hands-on', worksheets do not have a very high status, nevertheless they can be surprisingly useful, as experienced teachers well know. The focus of the photocopiable sheets in this section is therefore on the topics tackled in the QCA scheme of work for Year 1 which deal with mechanisms (moving pictures), structures (playgrounds and homes), and food (eat more fruit and vegetables).

Moving Ted (page 130)

Objective: To make a simple moving mechanism.

What to do: First photocopy or mount the bear onto card. Those children who are able should cut out the parts of Ted for themselves. Talk to the children and discuss what they might use to make Ted's legs or arms move. The objects in the toolbox provide some suggestions, but the children may find other ways (for example, a drawing pin pushed into the joint and into a wooden board will work two-dimensionally).

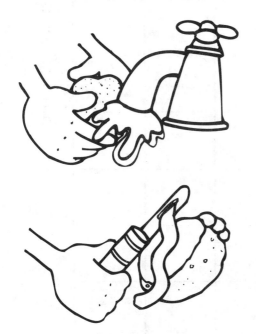

Differentiation: Limited dexterity is likely to be a problem for some children. Try photo-enlarging the bear and mounting it onto card. Let those who need it, practise making connections using strips of card, before attempting the bear. A hole punch can also be used with clips to make the moving lever. Let children experiment.

Extension: Challenge the children to draw a picture of themselves on card and to cut it out and make part of themselves move. Warn them not to draw too small.

See-saw (page 131)

Objective: To suggest an idea and explain what they are going to do (to make a simple lever mechanism).

What to do: *How can this be assembled so that we can make the cat and mouse move?* The children need to explain their ideas and describe what they are going to do. To avoid frustration, stick the pieces onto card. Discuss the ideas and introduce the word *pivot*. Once again, the objects in the toolbox are only there to offer suggestions.

Differentiation: Cut out the shapes for the less nimble-fingered children. Enlarging may also help.

Extension: *How could the see-saw be made stiffer?* Provide straws, pipe cleaners and sticky tape for this challenge. Let the children try out different ideas to see what works best.

Fruit and vegetables (page 132)

Objectives: To understand that there are many fruits and vegetables and that they all have separate names and to start to understand basic practices in food handling.

What to do: It is not necessary for the children to match the fruit and vegetables to the labels at the bottom of the sheet – they can report them orally. In a group or in a one-to-one situation with an adult, children point to and name the items. They then go on to answer the questions *Which would we peel before eating? Which would we wash before eating?* The children can record their answers on the sheet by writing the full words or just *P* or *W* (or both) by the side of each drawing. Discuss why we wash fruit and vegetables before eating.

Differentiation: This should be an oral exercise for less able children and they should not be required to write down the words (*P* or *W* will do). Handling and examining the real thing is the best way of supporting work on this sheet. If it is not possible or practical to have the full range of food available, choose two different fruits (or vegetables) to dissect and examine. *How are they different?*

Extension: This work links into learning about healthy eating and the need to eat more fruit and vegetables (according to the HEA, fruit and vegetables should form about a third of a balanced diet). Get the children to collect data about the amount of fruit and vegetables that they eat. They could display the results as a bar chart.

Houses can be different (page 133)

Objective: To observe that people live in different homes around the world and that there are reasons for the differences.

What to do: First ask the children to identify the houses on the sheet. Get them to describe the houses. *Do they have a special name?* The children provide describing words for the houses and write them underneath the houses in question. These do not have to be names or sentences, just words that are relevant. Thus they might supply the words *snow, ice, igloo, brick, detached,* and *garage*. There are words provided at the bottom of the page to help. Interrogate the pictures with the children and challenge them to say what the houses are constructed from, and why they might be different. For example, igloos are made from ice and snow because they are the only materials available. Tents are used because nomads move with their animals.

Differentiation: In this case it is mainly going to be differentiation by outcome. More able children will provide more rounded and detailed answers. Help less able children to record their answers – the quality of thinking is more important than the writing.

Extension: Ask the children to list parts of the house

that they live in (give examples) – such as *windows, doors, roof, chimney, brick, plaster, eaves, gutters* and so on. This could be a homework task.

Playtime (page 134)

Objectives: To investigate items of equipment found in a playground, to think about what they are made from and how they are put together. To design and build a model swing.

What to do: The first part of this sheet is straightforward observation that should be set in the context of classroom discussion and real observation. The children tick the equipment found in their playground (this need not be the school playground – choose a suitable site) and talk about what they are made from and how the parts are connected. The children then design and build a model swing (in pairs would be best). Make sure that the equipment required for this design-and-build exercise is available. A suitable construction kit is essential. *How can the design be tested?*

Differentiation: A visit to a suitable playground is essential for less able children. Take photographs of the equipment. Name the equipment. Examine what it is made from and how it is put together. After such work, the worksheet should not prove difficult.

Extension: Challenge the children to make other playground equipment using construction kits and other materials (a see-saw, a climbing frame and so on). Discuss the progress of this work with the children and tease out the problems. *How can it be made more stable?* And so on. Get each group to contribute to the solutions.

Moving Ted

Can you find a way of making Ted's arms or legs move?
The objects in the toolbox may help you.

See-saw

- Can you make the see-saw move up and down? Where does the see-saw **pivot**?
- What might you use from the toolbox?

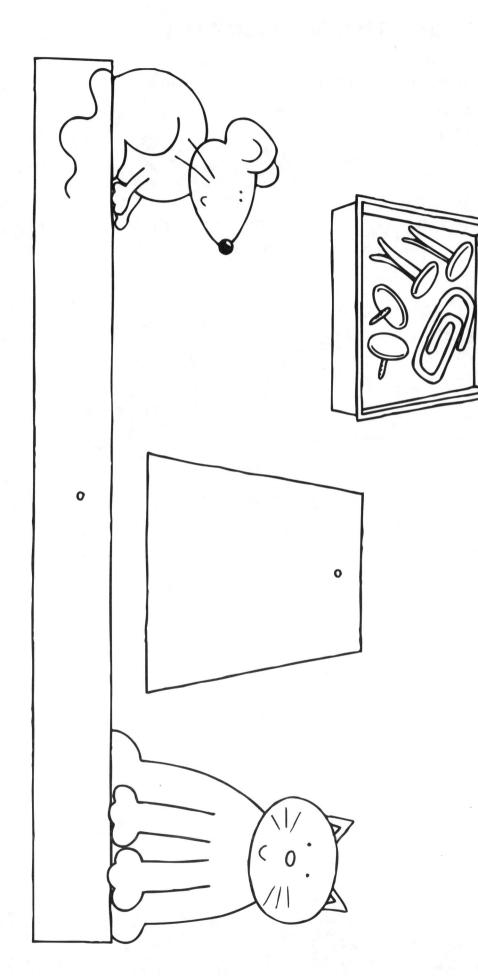

Fruit and vegetables

- What are the fruit and vegetables below called?

- Which do we **wash** before eating? W

- Which do we **peel** before eating? P

$\boxed{\text{carrot}}$ $\boxed{\text{banana}}$ $\boxed{\text{tomato}}$ $\boxed{\text{apple}}$ $\boxed{\text{strawberry}}$

$\boxed{\text{leek}}$ $\boxed{\text{orange}}$ $\boxed{\text{potato}}$ $\boxed{\text{pear}}$ $\boxed{\text{cauliflower}}$

Houses can be different

Think of words to describe these houses. What are they made from? Why are they different?

| igloo | stilts | tent | brick |

| detached | snow | sand | water |

Playtime

● Tick the ones you can find in your playground. What are they called? Find out what they are made from. How have the parts been joined together?

● Design and build a model swing. What will you use?

(construction kit)   (cardboard)   (egg box)   (string)

ICT

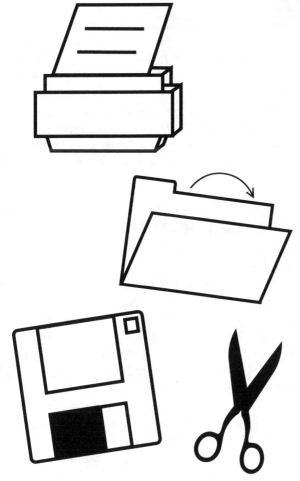

Reading pictures (page 137)

Objectives: To understand that pictures provide information and that computers use icons to provide information and instructions.

What to do: Tell the children they need to 'read' the pictures and say what information they convey to us. They should write underneath the picture what it indicates, using the words in the labels below each set of pictures to help them if necessary. Single word answers are acceptable. *Why are pictures used instead of words?* Introduce the term *icon*.

Differentiation: Those children who cannot cope with the words and the writing should tell the answers to an adult. Alternatively, they could work in a small group, perhaps in pairs, charged with the task of agreeing answers to the problem. They then report their answers to an adult.

Extension: More able children might write down where they would expect to find these pictures. Children could add some 'information pictures' of their own to another sheet of paper. They could design a picture sign for homework and bring it to school. Other children have to guess what the icon stands for.

Icon chart (page 138)

Objectives: To understand that pictures provide information and that computers use icons to provide information and instructions.

What to do: Children should have access to a computer for this photocopiable worksheet and work directly from the screen. It may be sensible for you to set up the program from which they will work. They choose five icons and record them on the sheet as shown in the first example.

Differentiation: Less confident children should work in pairs to tackle this problem and if necessary should have adult support as well. Children should find out by doing: *What happens if I place the cursor on this icon? What happens if I click on this icon?*

Extension: Children could work on a website's homepage that uses a range of icons.

Sorting animals (page 139)

Objective: To understand that objects can be divided according to criteria.

What to do: Here the children have to allocate the animals to the correct set. Make sure that they understand what each set is. Tell them that they are simply going to sort these animals out and put them where they belong. Some might belong in both places.

In the terminology of the National Curriculum, ICT is a statutory, non-core, foundation subject at Key Stage 1. Key Stage 1 is when children learn to use ICT confidently, become familiar with hardware and software, and use it to develop their ideas and record their creative work. The four aspects of study given in the National Curriculum are 'Finding things out'; 'Developing ideas and making things happen'; 'Exchanging and sharing information'; 'Reviewing, modifying and evaluating work as it progresses'. There is also a statutory requirement to use ICT across the curriculum. All this is a pretty tall order and the QCA scheme provides six units to cope with it, although no time estimate for their completion is given.

For the most part ICT requires technology, normally a computer or an electronic robot, and by its very nature is not a pencil-and-paper subject, which leaves limited scope for the use of photocopiable worksheets. But the following have been constructed to help teachers cope with some of the work demanded by the National Curriculum that is covered in the QCA Scheme of Work (units 1A to 1F). Follow-up work is suggested but there is always scope for moving onto an activity involving a computer.

Where should they be placed? The children can allocate the animals to the correct set by drawing a connecting line; by drawing pictures in the sets themselves; or by cutting out the pictures and sticking them into the sets.

Differentiation: Cut out (roughly will do) the animals and let less able children sort and sift and then stick. Enlarge the sets if the operation appears too fiddly for the children. It may be useful to examine each animal with the children, naming as you go along. A range of picture reference books on hand would be useful.

Extension: This whole activity is about labelling and sorting according to set criteria. Give children another similar activity such as animals that fly/ animals that don't, machines that move/machines that don't, children in class X/children in class Y and so on. Make large displays of 'sorted' objects complete with labels to show that objects can be sorted by the use of key words.

Favourite colours (page 140)

Objectives: To collect data and to create a simple pictogram and to appreciate that ICT can be used to do this.

What to do: First explain the format of the sheet and what its purpose is. The children are going to find out about the favourite colours of pupils in the class. Get them to colour in the 'heading' squares in the relevant colours first. The children then go to each child in turn and record their answer to the question, by colouring the appropriate square in the appropriate colour. Show children how to work systematically to avoid repetition (they could record the name of each child on the square to cover this point). On completion, interrogate the graphs with the children. *Which is the most popular colour in the class? Which is the least favourite colour?*

Differentiation: Less able children can mark the

selected squares with a coloured cross instead of fully colouring it in. Provide adult help if the task is still too challenging.

Extension: The next move is to produce a pictogram or similar graph, using a suitable graphing program. There are a number available (such as *Graph it* – consult your ICT co-ordinator if in doubt). A good challenge is to get the children to sort 'attribute blocks' (coloured plastic shapes that can be sorted according to a number of criteria – size, colour, thickness) and to produce a graph on the computer. Discuss why they might choose to make a graph this way rather than by hand.

Push, pull or twist (page 141)

Objective: To recognise that machines and devices must be controlled.

What to do: One example has been completed on the photocopiable sheet. Show the children the example and explain why the arrow has been drawn. Let them draw arrows in the same way for the other machines. Some devices use more than one. There is a blank box for the children to draw their own device.

Differentiation: For those who have difficulty, you should ensure that they know what the various machines are. Then demonstrate a variety of controlling mechanisms (operate the TV; unlock your car; switch on the photocopier; make a phone-call). They also need to know what the words in the middle of the sheet mean.

Extension: *How can we make things happen?* Give children this technical challenge in relation to some (non-hazardous) household technology. Ask them to find out from adults and then have a 'tell the class' session. Do they know how to: make a phone call; operate the doorbell; tune in the radio; switch off the computer safely?

Reading pictures

● What do these pictures tell us?

_____   _____

_____   _____

(no swimming)   (toilets)   (bumpy road)   (telephone)

● What do these computer icons tell us?

 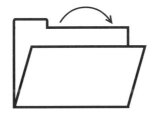  

____ ____   ____ ____   ____ ____   ____ ____

(cut)   (print)   (save)   (open)

Icon chart

- Look at the computer screen and make a chart of some **icons**.
- Write what they mean.

Icon	means
	print

Put the animals in the correct sets.

Sorting animals

These live in **the sea**.

These live **on the land**.

Favourite colours

Ask your friends to choose a favourite colour. Colour in a square.

red								
blue								
yellow								
green								
orange								
pink								

Push, pull or twist

● How do you operate these? The first one has been done for you.

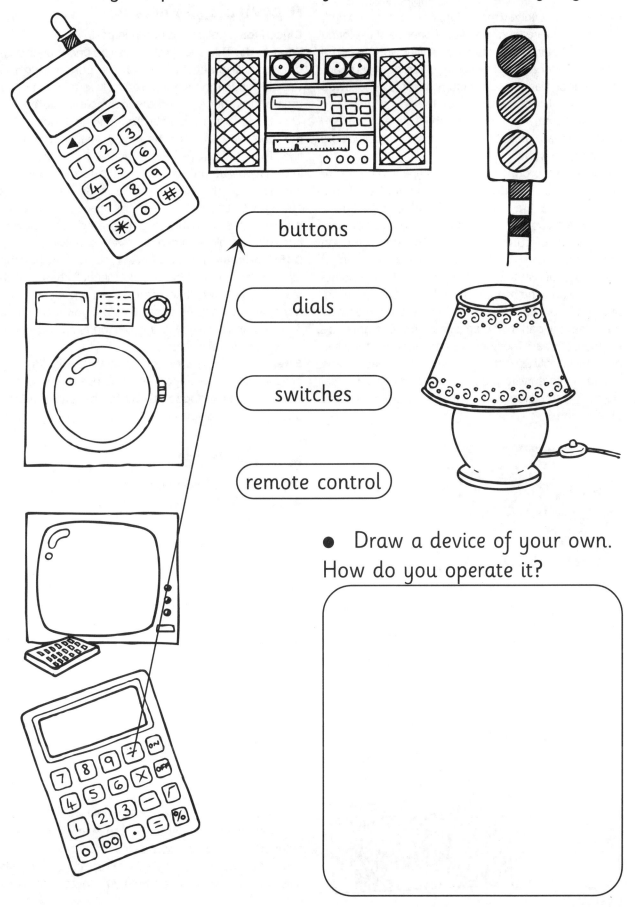

buttons

dials

switches

remote control

● Draw a device of your own. How do you operate it?

ART AND DESIGN

Art and design is one of those subjects where the 'how' is very definitely more significant than the 'what'. What children are taught is the experience of exploring a range of starting points for practical work, using a range of materials, and exploring different kinds of art. The familiar National Curriculum formula is followed for this subject, thus 'knowledge, skills, and understanding' requires that children *explore and develop ideas; investigate and make; and evaluate and develop work*.

QCA have produced a fairly compact scheme for art and design, compressing the work for Year 1 into three units that are allocated a total of up to 32 hours. The expectation is that each unit will be given at least eight hours of curriculum time. The units, though compact, cover a great deal. The collection of photocopiables in this section provide starting points for work within the scope defined by the QCA scheme, but they should not be constrained to the limits of an A4 sheet of paper. Pictures can, for example, be enlarged. Regard the sheets as a resource – they can be more flexibly used than standard worksheets. Some provide children with the opportunity to examine real works of art, albeit through the medium of the photograph.

© Corel

Clemens August as Falconer by Pieter Horemans

© Corel

School Boy by Albert Anker (1875)

A portrait (1) (page 144)

Objective: To focus attention on portraits.

What to do: This sheet might well be undertaken as a group or class activity. Look at the portrait. *What is this?* Introduce the word *portrait*. Have they ever had their portrait done? Read the incomplete sentence – *This man is...* Invite the children to think of words that describe the man, how he looks, what he might be like. This is about reading a picture to get as much information out of it as possible. Make a list of all the suggestions. The children write these into the box provided. Get them to imitate the pose (you can go to great lengths over this to get as much accuracy as possible, equally you can do it very simply).

Differentiation: All children will love acting out the picture and it might help to do this activity first with less able children, and then extract the descriptive words as the children pose. *Why are you pulling that face? What do you think this person is feeling? Is he rich? Important? Unhappy?*

Extension: Create a portrait gallery. Ask children to bring in their favourite portrait of themselves to school. Why did they choose it? Write the explanations underneath for display purposes.

A portrait (2) (page 145)

Objective: To focus attention on portraits.

What to do: This sheet should receive the same treatment as the previous one, however, the portrait here is of a child, possibly the same age as the children themselves. Ask the children questions about the way the clothes are worn (and how they are different to their own school uniforms), the pose (note his hands are in his pockets), and how the artist shows us what sort of boy this is.

Differentiation/extension: Follow a similar approach to the above activity. Extend the children's understanding by asking questions about why portraits are made. *Why did the artist paint this picture?*

In the mirror (page 146)

Objective: To record self-portraits from observation.

What to do: Explain the instructions on the sheet. You will need a good-sized mirror for this activity, a little hand mirror will not do. Talk about how the children might complete the sentences, then let them draw a self-portrait. The self-portrait can be done in many ways, it is for you to decide, but most children of this age would want to work on a bigger canvas than A4 so be prepared to enlarge the sheet. There is no reason why they can't do a 'try drawing' or sketch in pencil on the sheet first and then a larger painted or crayoned picture executed on bigger paper. Talk about how they might improve their work.

Differentiation: Restrict choices to make it easier for less able children. Make sure that the mirror allows for a decent head-and-shoulders view only. Encourage the children to try – make sure that they understand that they cannot do it 'wrong' although they might improve their work later. It is helpful to show children a range of self-portraits that they can look at and talk about. This is the sort of central resource that the school might build up for repeated use.

Extension: Ask the children to describe how they would like to be shown in a portrait. *What clothes would you wear? What would you be doing? Are you cheerful? Shy?* Children need to explore different ways of making marks, so you might set a challenge such as: *What is the best way of showing a piece of material (clothing) in a portrait?* Let them try different ways of doing this and discuss their results.

Spot the fabric (page 147)

Objective: To understand what is meant by a fabric.

What to do: Make sure that the children understand the words in the two boxes on the sheet. Get the children to draw connecting lines from the objects to the correct term – *fabric* or *something else*. Note that *fabric* is the root of *fabrication*. Children need to appreciate that fabrics are made.

Differentiation: Differentiation will be by outcome. More able children will spot that all of the objects are constructed of several materials - *fabric* and *something else* – their sheet should become a labyrinth of lines. Encourage more able children to name some of the other non-fabric materials, such as wood and plastic.

Extension: Make a 'hands-on' display of different fabrics for the children to look at and touch. How many different fabrics can they identify in the classroom? Give them labels marked 'fabric' (Post-it Notes will do) and let them stick them on the fabrics they find.

Sculpture (1) (page 148)

Objectives: To understand what a sculpture is and to make comments about a work of sculpture.

What to do: Interrogate the picture with the children (a group activity), using the questions on the sheet as prompts. Introduce the word *sculpture* and ask the children what they think a sculpture is. (You don't need to give them a definition.) Talk about the materials that are used by sculptors. *Why are they chosen?* Let them explore the possibilities of making a similar sculpture using clay.

Differentiation: Sculpture has to be experienced and some children may struggle to get to grips with the concept if they haven't experienced many examples. Try to give children this experience. Can you borrow from the Museum Service? Can you visit a gallery? Is there a sculpture to be admired in your area? Studying sculpture has to be experience driven and it will not only be less able children who need to get 'hands-on'. If the children find clay a bit daunting, there are other materials (Plasticine, for example) that can be used. Clay is undoubtedly best for this one.

Extension: Challenge the children to make a sculpture of their favourite animal using materials they collect or are given. What ideas do the materials suggest to them? This approach will work well if it arises from lots of talking, examining materials, looking for naturally occurring shapes, and so on. It cannot be done cold! Ask them to find out some names of famous sculptors as a homework task.

Sculpture (2) (page 149)

Objectives: To understand what a sculpture is and to make comments about a work of sculpture.

What to do: This shows an abstract sculpture – an entirely different sort to 'Sculpture (1)', but the approach should be exactly the same as the previous sheet. Again, focus on what the children think the sculpture is made of. *What is it? What is it for?*

Differentiation/extension: As above but get the children to make their own abstract sculpture as an extension activity.

A portrait (1)

© Corel

Clemens August as Falconer by Pieter Horemans

- What is this man doing?

- What sort of person do you think he is?

- Can you describe what he is wearing?

- Why do you think he had his picture painted?

- Can you pose like this?

This man is...

A portrait (2)

© Corel

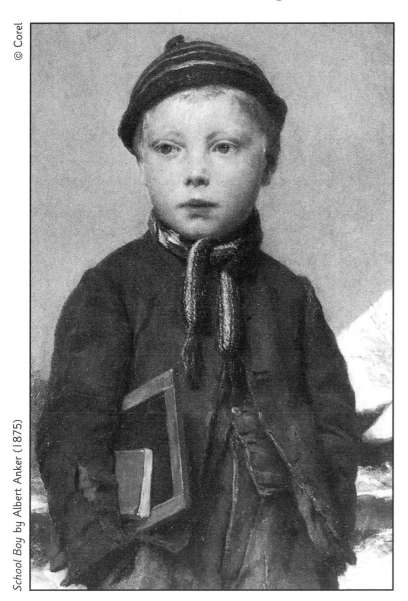

School Boy by Albert Anker (1875)

- Look at this boy's face.

- How old do you think he is? How can you tell?

- What is he doing?

- Can you describe what he is wearing?

- Can you pose like this?

This boy is...

In the mirror

● Look at yourself in the mirror. Describe what you see.

I am _____

_____

I have _____

_____

I look like _____

_____

● Draw your own self-portrait here.

Spot the fabric

Draw lines to show what these objects are made from.

fabric

something else

Sculpture (1)

- What is it?
- Who made it? Why?
- What do you think it is made of?
- Where would you put it?

- Make a sculpture of your own like this.

Sculpture (2)

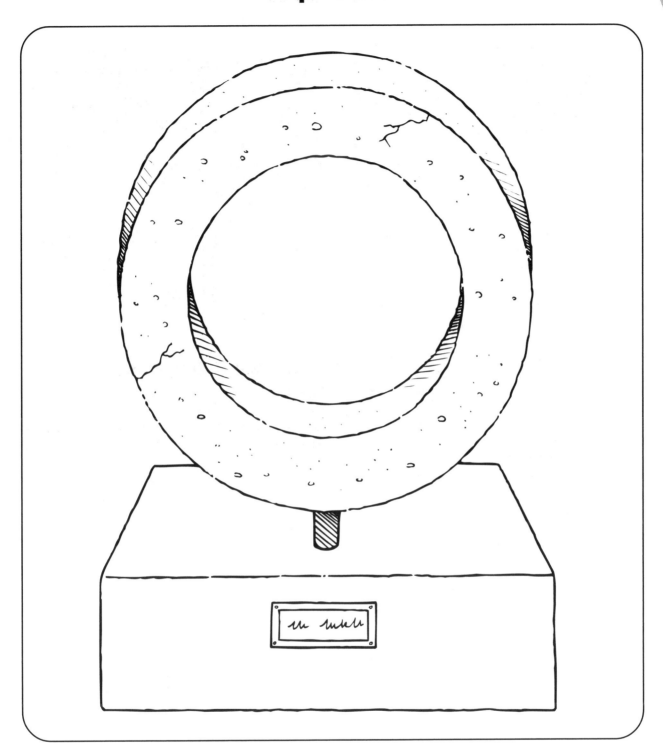

- What is it?
- Who made it? Why?
- What do you think it is made of?
- Where would you put it?

- Make a sculpture of your own like this.

MUSIC

In theory, at any rate, music will be given a great deal of curriculum time at Key Stage 1. The QCA Scheme of Work covers the whole key stage in seven units, which are allocated up to six hours each, except the first unit, 'Ongoing skills', which is allocated eighteen hours. Singing, dancing, listening to music and playing instruments are clearly going to be a major part of a young child's experience of school, and hardly a day should go by without a musical experience of some sort.

The emphasis has to be on experience, for knowledge and understanding of music will come through an active curriculum of *performing, composing* and *appraising*. National Curriculum requirements are for a child to learn to control sounds through singing and playing (performing); to create and develop musical ideas (composing); and to make improvements to their own work (appraising). These all involve activities that the worksheets in this section can support. Worksheets cannot reproduce sound, so the number of worksheet possibilities are limited for this age group. It is also the case that these sheets, more than most sheets in other sections, lend themselves to large-group or even class usage. Telling the story of Little Red Riding Hood, for example, will be more fun and more valuable an experience if it is tackled in a large group with children taking turns at the different parts. Similarly 'Making sounds', (page 153), can lead to the creation of a class 'body' orchestra. Making music is very often a social activity.

Little Red Riding Hood (page 152)

Objective: To use their voices in different ways, for example singing, whispering.

What to do: Telling a story is not much fun without an audience so it is desirable that the children do this sheet within groups. In fact, a group of eight children could take one picture each and tell the story 'round the circle'. Each picture represents part of the well-known story and the children tell the part illustrated but they must use different types of voices for the characters. The idea is to help children to find the

different voices that they have (and eventually their singing voice). After telling the story, the children should identify and describe the types of voices, using the words at the bottom of the sheet to help them.

Differentiation: More able children may be capable of telling the whole story to the class on their own but some children will need help in identifying the different voices. Demonstrate a number of different voices to them – whisper instructions, shout good morning – talk about what is appropriate for each task. Have a 'best wolf voice' competition.

Extension: Move into the realm of the singing voice. Response games based on a minor third are easily contrived and can be regularly repeated (G and E or F and D). For example, Teacher: *Is Holly having lunch today?* (D FF DD F F D); Holly: *Yes, I am.* (F F D); Class: *Yes, she is.* (F F D).

Making sounds (page 153)

Objective: To explore different sounds that can be made using hands, feet, mouth and so on.

What to do: This is a noisy one, a sheet that is best done as a class exercise – then at least nobody is disturbed! Lead the group and describe what is going on in the picture. As you do, the class (or group) make the appropriate noise. Get the children to agree on which is the best part of the body to use to make the noises. Children write in the word for the part used into the balloons on the sheet. As a grand anarchic finale, get the class to make all the noises at once, then retire to a darkened room with a bottle of aspirins!

Differentiation: Some of the children will need encouragement to use different parts of their body to make the noises. Go through each of the pictures at the top of the page before you start, and explore what sounds can be made with each part of the body.

Extension: Move on to explore rhythm using hands or feet, fingers or tongue. Clap or tap the rhythms of phrases with the children, for example *head and knees*. Tap on the parts of the body named. Tap out rhythms of songs known to the children such as 'Jack and Jill went up the hill'. Can they guess the song from the rhythm? Let them join in. Vary the speed sometimes. Make sure the children have lots of practice.

Long and short sounds (page 154)

Objectives: To explore duration and to use their voices to make long and short sounds.

What to do: The sounds are linked in long and short pairs. Children have to identify the sounds from the pictures and recognise which is the long one and which is the short. They indicate their choice by drawing a connecting line to the key words *long* and *short*.

Differentiation: The words are there to assist the

teacher as much as anything else, but you may want to read them out to some children. With less able children, tease out the correct describing words from the illustrations (an adult can identify the written word for the child). Get them to imitate the sounds as best they can to appreciate the different durations. All the sounds can be reproduced in the classroom (except the dog who will have to be imitated).

Extension: Give children the opportunity to explore long and short sounds using readily available classroom instruments – drum, chime bars and so on. The chime bar makes a long sound. *How can we make it produce a short sound?* (By stopping the vibrations with our hand.) Tell a story and add long and short sound effects. Get the children to distinguish between them, for example 'Hickory, dickory, dock' – the mouse running, the chime of the clock and so on.

Higher and lower (page 155)

Objectives: To follow pitch movement and to sing, moving up or down, following changes in pitch.

What to do: After looking at the pictures, the children sing (in their head is a good skill to develop) the opening phrase of the song. They then have to match the pattern of the phrase with the pattern of the dots given on the sheet, by drawing a line.

Differentiation: Those children who fail to recognise the songs from the words and pictures will need adult support. Sing the songs to them. Demonstrate the changing pitch by using hand signals. Can they match your signals to the dots?

Extension: You can play lots of games with pitch, and familiarity with them will help to develop the children's ability to discriminate reliably. Sing simple phrases and get the children to match, with you, the sounds to hand signals. Sometimes demonstrate small steps, sometimes leaps. Play notes on a piano or chime bar and follow it with another. When you play high to low, the children sit down; when you play low to high, they stand up. (Non-specialists do sometimes feel insecure in this subject. Don't be afraid to consult the music coordinator or a music scheme for ideas.)

Little Red Riding Hood

● Tell the story. Use different voices for each character.

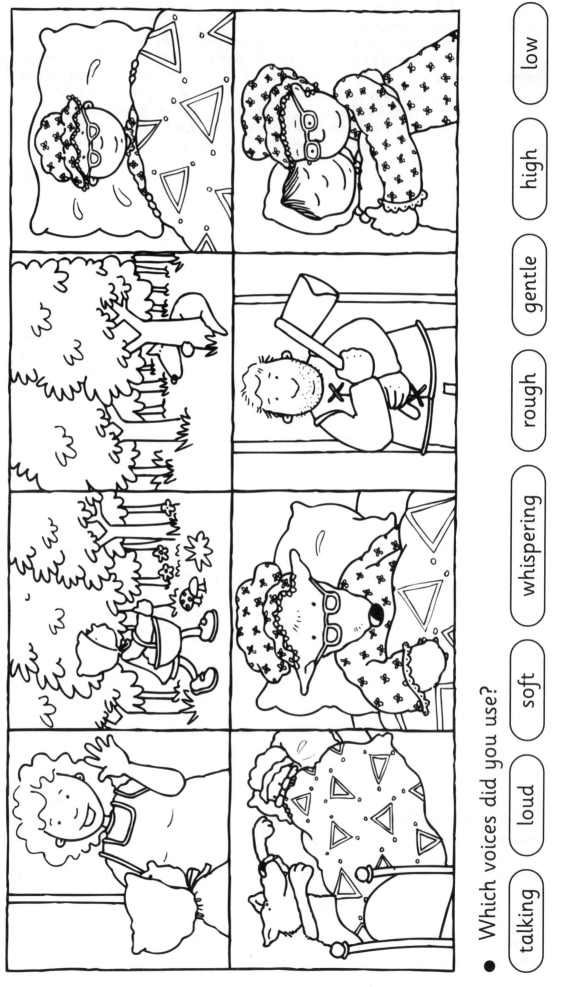

● Which voices did you use?

talking　loud　soft　whispering　rough　gentle　high　low

Making sounds

Make the sounds in this picture. What will you use to make the sounds?

voice

lips

tongue

teeth

hands

feet

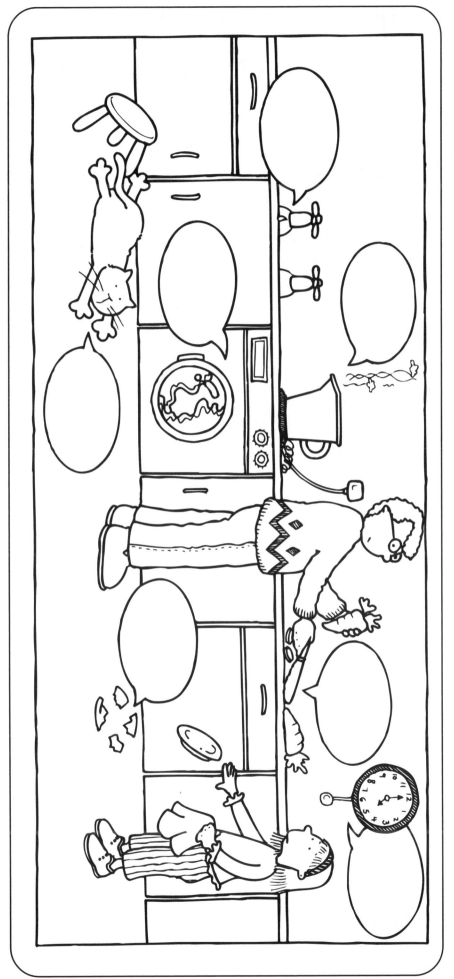

Long and short sounds

Which sound is **long** and which is **short**? The first one has been done for you.

ticking and chiming

long

short

hammering and sawing

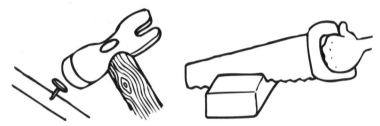

long

short

knocking and ringing

long

short

dripping and running

long

short

barking and growling

long

short

Higher and lower

Match the dots to the songs.

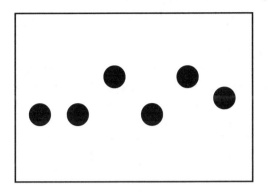

Three blind mice

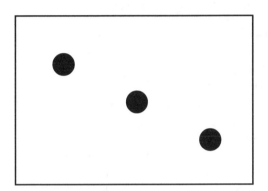

London's burning

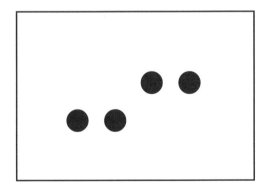

Twinkle, twinkle little star

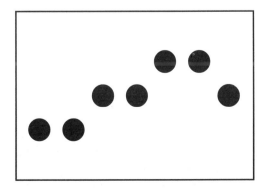

Happy Birthday to you

RELIGIOUS EDUCATION

Although there are 12 National Curriculum subjects (from September 2002, including citizenship at Key Stages 3 and 4), religious education is not one of them. RE is, however, a *statutory requirement* and must be taught according to a locally agreed syllabus in all maintained schools (except voluntary-aided and schools of a religious character where religion is taught according to a trust deed or guidelines).

The QCA scheme, which the following photocopiable worksheets support, is substantial. It has no less than six units for Year 1 and suggests an indicated teaching time of 36 hours in total. The scheme emphasises that not only is there no compulsion to use it, but that schools might opt to pick and choose material from it in order to meet the demands of the locally agreed syllabus. Teachers should treat these worksheets in the same way. Ignore those sheets that do not apply and amend, or add to, those sheets that do not quite fit the needs of your school. Where questions about a particular faith community are involved, rather than general (generic) information, advice is best sought from members of the faith community themselves, especially when further detailed information is required. Following the pattern of the QCA scheme, some of the worksheets are generic (such as dealing with 'belonging' in general terms) whilst others move on to the specific (for example, dealing with 'belonging' to a particular faith).

Belonging (page 158)

Objective: To identify ways in which they belong and to consolidate their understanding of the word.

What to do: Explain to the children what they have to do by showing them the example that is on the sheet. In the example a blank space has been left for the children to fill in their family name (surname) and to draw a picture of their family. Talk about 'belonging'. Each child belongs to the class, the school, the village/town and so on. They will choose to belong to other groups such as Sunday School or the dance club. The children should write the names of these groups in the blank squares and draw small pictures to indicate what the group is.

Differentiation: Some examples of groups that children may belong to are provided at the bottom of the sheet. Read these out to the less able children. More able children

might write a sentence about each group or state one fact about it. (*It meets Thursday. My best friend goes to dance.*)

Extension: Start a class book about 'The groups we belong to.' Get children to bring pictures and artefacts relating to the group. Use photocopies of these for display purposes, especially if they are precious. Ask the children to give talks about a group they belong to and show objects connected with it. For example, a child might talk about a gymnastics club, bring along photographs, badges and trophies and even demonstrate what has been learned at the club.

Belonging: religion (1) (page 159)

Objectives: To understand that religious people belong to a faith and to identify some of the ways in which this belonging is demonstrated.

What to do: This sheet, and the two that follow, build on work done on 'belonging' previously: the extension of the idea of belonging to a family to belonging to a religious family or faith community. *How do people show that they belong to this sort of family?* Talk about this idea first. Some children will belong to a faith community, others will not. You should build upon the experience of the children in the class. Talk about what is shown on the sheet and the two groups (in this case, Christianity and Judaism). *Which picture goes with which group?* The children connect the pictures to the religion by drawing lines. (NB: There is no escaping the fact that some children will find this sheet extremely easy while others will find it very challenging, depending on their experience.) If these religions are part of your syllabus, you should make sure that the appropriate teaching precedes the use of this sheet. The pictures shown are: font/baptism, church, cross (Christianity); and Magen David (the Star of David), kippah (skull cap), and menorah (seven-branched candlestick) (Judaism).

Differentiation: Differentiation may well be by religion here – knowledge will divide. You do not have to explore the symbols of belonging too deeply at this stage, merely make sure that the children can identify which religion each is connected to. As far as is possible, support children by experience. Show them objects and places, if possible.

Extension: Where you go from here must depend upon your particular agreed syllabus and the experiences of the children in the class. But the most desirable approach is to explore more fully what it means to belong to the faiths identified, using the children's own experiences and visiting adults. Investigate what people do in *one* religion, using books, visits, and videos.

Belonging: religion (2) (page 160)

Objectives: To understand that religious people belong to a faith and to identify some of the ways in which this belonging is demonstrated.

What to do: Everything that has been said about the previous activity applies here. The three sheets together in this section provide opportunities for teachers to choose which is the most appropriate to use in their situation. The aim is the same. The two religions here are Hinduism and Islam. The pictures show: hijab (headscarf), mosque, star and crescent moon, prayer cap (Islam); aum symbol, mandir (temple) (Hinduism).

Differentiation/extension: See above.

Belonging: religion (3) (page 161)

Objectives: To understand that religious people belong to a faith and to identify some of the ways in which this belonging is demonstrated.

What to do: See above. The two religions here are Sikhism and Buddhism. The pictures show: Gurdwara (place of worship), kangha (special comb), kara (steel bracelet) (Sikhism); lotus plant, eight-spoked Dhamma wheel, Buddha (Buddhism).

Differentiation/extension: See above.

Christmas gifts (page 162)

Objectives: To know the Christmas story and to understand why Christians give gifts at Christmas.

What to do: Cut out the cartoon pictures of the Christmas story. It is advisable to mount the pictures on card if they are to be used again. Challenge the children to place the pictures into the correct sequence of the Christmas story. They complete the blank square with a picture of a present they think suitable for Jesus. (You can support them here as appropriate, for example *What would a carpenter give to Jesus? What presents might we give to a baby today?*)

Differentiation: Use picture story books, a crib model (if you have one) or any other means to tell the story to those children whose knowledge of it is insecure. Write up questions on a flip chart or board for more able children to tackle, such as: *What gifts did the wisemen give Jesus? Why do Christians give gifts at Christmas?* Provide help with vocabulary.

Extension: Christians believe that Jesus is God's gift to the world and that is why they give gifts at Christmas. Difficult religious notions begin to appear here and they can only be approached through children's experiences, feelings and discussion. Talk about giving and receiving. Talk about why giving is an important part of a Christian's celebration of Christmas. Get children to act out the Christmas story (or parts of it).

Belonging: Christianity (page 163)

Objectives: To recognise ways in which belonging to Christianity is demonstrated and to learn that baptism is the way that some Christians welcome babies into the family of Jesus.

What to do: Building on the notion that belonging to a faith is like belonging to another sort of family, discuss how people show that they belong to the Christian church. Use the experience of children in the class. The sheet is straightforward – children connect the label to the correct picture, and complete the sentence at the bottom, for example *I wear school uniform because I belong to St Jude's School.* (NB: Not all churches within the Christian faith use child baptism as a sign of entry into the church.)

Differentiation: Provide adult support for the language aspects of this sheet.

Extension: Some church leaders may be willing to demonstrate a baptism using a doll. Certainly follow-up should include a visit to a church to see a font and understand what happens in a baptism service. (The font is near the entrance to the church because it is used to welcome children/babies into the Christian church.) Ask the children to find out how babies were welcomed into their family.

Churches (page 164)

Objective: To recognise what a church looks like.

What to do: Talk about the pictures. *What do they show? Have you seen any buildings like these?* (The buildings are cathedral; Salvation Army citadel; Methodist chapel; country church; and modern town church.) If you do this as a class exercise using the experiences of all the children, you may be able to name some of the buildings. Refer children to the vocabulary at the bottom of the sheet for clues. Get them to draw a church that they know in the blank box.

Differentiation: Drawing from memory is not easy. Ideally, walk your area with the children, look at churches and return with clipboards and sketching pencils to draw the building.

Extension: Ask the children to draw one part of a church and to say what it is they have drawn. Visit a local church and divide into groups to produce sketches of different parts, inside and out. *What are they? What are they for?*

Belonging

Which groups do you belong to? Draw them. Name them.

I belong to

the _____ family

I belong to

_____

I belong to

_____

I belong to

_____

Beavers   Brownies   school   class   friends

Belonging: religion (1)

Which pictures belong to which religion?

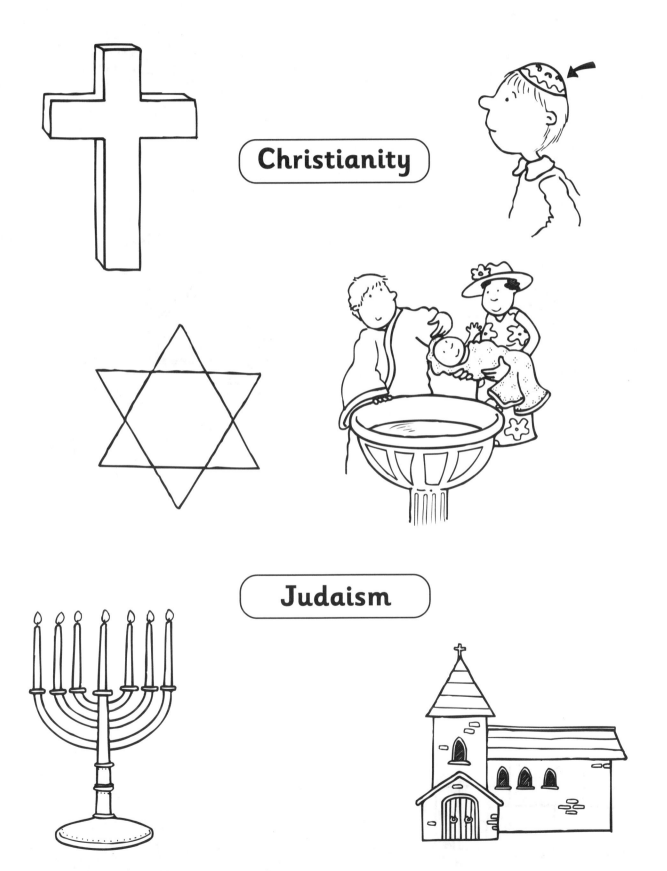

Christianity

Judaism

SCHOLASTIC   159

Belonging: religion (2)

Which pictures belong to which religion?

Hinduism

Islam

Belonging: religion (3)

Which pictures belong to which religion?

Sikhism

Buddhism

Christmas gifts

Belonging: Christianity

● Match these labels to the pictures.

(baptism candle)   (cross)   (fish badge)   (font)

● Complete this sentence.

I wear _____ because

I belong to _____.

Churches

What are these? Do you know a building like any of these?

(church) (chapel) (hall) (tower) (town) (country)

PSHE AND CITIZENSHIP

PSHE and citizenship is a subject that overarches other subjects and can be taught through and alongside material that the National Curriculum identifies elsewhere. The reason why this subject has to be considered separately is to ensure that it is not inadvertently neglected. PSHE and citizenship is too important to be ignored but it is not a National Curriculum subject for Key Stages 1 and 2. Schools are, nevertheless, expected to promote spiritual, moral, social and cultural development across the National Curriculum at all key stages. To this end, the government provided a non-statutory framework for PSHE and citizenship at Key Stages 1 and 2.

These photocopiable worksheets fit learning targets from this framework under its headings: 'Developing confidence and responsibility and making the most of their abilities'; 'Preparing to play an active role as citizens'; 'Developing a healthy, safer lifestyle'; 'Developing good relationships and respecting differences between people'. The worksheets are only small pieces in a very large jigsaw but they do fit very neatly into the overall picture of PSHE and citizenship. Although the National Curriculum framework helps, teachers should also be clear about the aims and ethos of their particular school.

Welcome to our school (page 168)

Objective: To observe the local environment and to say how it might be improved.

What to do: First explain to the children what the sheet is about. *In what ways is the school welcoming?* Ideally take the children to the school entrance – this could be the main (exterior) entrance if the weather is suitable for outside work and there is sufficient supervision, or the school lobby or reception area. *When a visitor arrives what would make them feel welcome?* Read out the words in the 'Things to think about' to direct the children's thinking. Finally, the children draw a picture (or diagram) of the entrance showing all the welcoming things. Get them to write suggestions for improvement on the back of the sheet. Clearly there is scope to draw a second 'plan' showing how it could be improved.

Differentiation: Some children will need to be given a more hands-on experience of the entrance. Go through

the motions of enacting a visit to the school. *What signs do you notice? Who greets you? Do you know where to go and what to do?* Reliving the experience of a visitor (children could act out all the parts) will help to focus their attention on the problem presented on the sheet. Instead of drawing, a digital camera could be used to create images to be printed and mounted on the sheet. Discuss the problem of improvement.

Extension: Making things better is the challenge. Perhaps children could think about how they might make their classroom, their home, or their town/estate/village more welcoming. Divide the children into groups to deal with a particular aspect of the problem. Where possible, try to carry out some of the suggestions. *Why should we be welcoming?*

Good things about my friend
(page 169)

Objective: To develop confidence in expressing opinions about things that matter to them.

What to do: Encourage positive thinking. Concentrate on what is good about their friend. Discuss the problem before tackling the writing and encourage children to go beyond the superficial and trivial (for example, *She helps clear up the toys when she visits* is preferable to *She has blue eyes*). The portrait frame is intended for a positive image of the friend.

Differentiation: All children should manage this sheet although many will need help with writing down their 'three good things'. Provide adult support for less able children to write simple sentences, but you can accept single words if the meaning is clear. Non-writers could talk about their friend instead. They could present their answers to the class or record them on tape.

Extension: Tackle this exercise with 'friends' as the subject is relatively easy in social terms. Challenge the children to say one good thing about every member (friend or not) of their group or class. No negatives. This can be very affirming and encouraging for children with weak self-images. Make a display of the positive statements.

Keeping safe in school (page 170)

Objective: To make safe choices based on right/wrong, good/bad.

What to do: *What is happening in these pictures?* Discuss the scenes and why the actions are bad. If necessary, the children can use the phrases at the bottom of the page to help them. Talk about consequences. Do not accept *I mustn't do this because my teacher/mummy says so*. In the frame below the children should draw some other danger at school that they are aware of.

Differentiation: Less able children may need help with looking for other dangers. Focus their attention on a particular area – a school corridor/the dining hall/the playground. You may need to 'walk the ground' with them. Alternatively, collect pictures of other hazards (fire, hazardous litter, abandoned vehicles) to extend the sheet. *What are the hazards?* Be aware of school guidelines if drugs, smoking, or sexual issues are raised.

Extension: Follow up one area of concern. Road safety is the obvious one but there may be other matters that need addressing with your particular class (stranger danger/drugs). Get children to learn the 'Green Cross Code'.

Moving house
(page 171)

Objective: To recognise and name feelings – those associated with change.

What to do: Talk about moving house. Has anybody in the class moved recently? What happened? How did they feel about it? Explain that the people on the sheet have different feelings about moving. *Because* is the critical word. Make sure that the children understand the sentences and read the words at the bottom of the page to them. They should select the most appropriate word and write it into the space provided.

Differentiation: This can be very difficult for less able children because of the reading problem. Tackle this sheet in a group with an adult 'reader' to assist. Children may also need help understanding what the various feelings are. Play a game where you act out a feeling and the children have to guess how you feel. Do the obvious ones – happy, sad, angry and so on. Go through the feeling words at the bottom of the page, one at a time, sorting out meanings.

Extension: Explore different feelings. Ask the children to think about how they would feel if – someone stole their toy, they lost a glove, they had a puppy for Christmas, someone hurt them. Chose a relevant situation and ask them to explain their feelings to the class.

Right ways and wrong ways
(page 172)

Objective: To know how to behave in different situations.

What to do: Look at the pictures and put a tick or cross at the side (in the box) depending on whether the action is the right way or the wrong way. This is a good sheet to tackle with a group. Discuss the situations. Get the children to say *It is wrong because*…

Differentiation: This is a sheet requiring no reading skills and should be accessible to all children. Adult intervention in the discussion should be controlled. Let the children do most of the talking!

Extension: Make a list of school rules for 'good manners'. Ask children to make up one school rule each – this could be a homework task.

Permission
(page 173)

Objective: To learn to ask for and to give permission, listening to other people and playing and working cooperatively.

What to do: Cut out and mount both the large and small wheels on card. Using a fastener, attach the small wheel to the centre of the large wheel so that it will rotate easily. By rotating the inner wheel the children can construct questions beginning *Please may I...?* In small groups, the children take it in turns to spin their wheel to make a question. The group has to decide yes or no and then explain why. Provide adult intervention – the adult can play devil's advocate and give a negative answer but the children must challenge them to explain why.

Differentiation: Children of all abilities should cope with this sheet if the exercise is set up properly. Encourage the more able children to make the wheel for themselves if their cutting is up to the challenge.

Extension: Get the class to make a list of other times that they need to ask permission. You could add some times when you need to ask permission yourself. Put the list up on display.

I am good at... (page 174)

Objective: To develop confidence by recognising what they are good at.

What to do: With the whole class, talk about the kind of different things that people are good at. Discuss your own skills (focus on skills not weaknesses). The children choose three areas of competence from the 'stamps' on the sheet. They cut out the pictures, stick them into the blank spaces and write the word on the line. The children then add a choice of their own by drawing into the extra blank at the bottom.

Differentiation: Less able children should cope with the picture exercise but those with more developed writing skills should be expected to complete the sentences. Lines are provided next to the pictures on the sheet for this purpose.

Extension: Take the sheet and change the 'I' for the name of a friend or another child in the class, for example *Toby is good at...* Then repeat the exercise. You can use this to improve class bonding and to raise a particular individual's self-esteem.

Mistakes (page 175)

Objectives: To learn from their experiences and know that it is all right to make mistakes. To learn how their behaviour affects others.

What to do: Children simply tick yes or no next to the statements on the sheet. However, the value of the exercise lies in the talk that goes with it, so it is suggested that this is carried out as a group exercise. The answers do need examination. It is all right to tread on the cat, by accident, but not as a deliberate act. The message must be 'Mistakes are allowed'.

Although we are focusing on 'accidents' and building confidence (not to fear making errors), there is also opportunity to talk about actions that affect others.

Differentiation: Some children will need more discussion of the questions. Be aware that adults are not always rational and benign and children may well have experienced being 'told off' for making a mistake. Explain how this happens – for example we don't always know whether somebody has bumped into us accidentally or on purpose in the playground.

Extension: Children can make up an illustrated poem in the same format as the lines on the sheet.

Feelings (page 176)

Objective: To recognise and name feelings.

What to do: Children suggest what they think Fred is feeling, judging by the look on his face.

Differentiation: More able children can choose words from the bottom of the page and write these next to the appropriate face. Acceptable alternatives can also be written. For the rest it becomes an oral exercise although an adult could write the words down for the children for them to copy. The sheet will have more value if done as a group exercise.

Extension: Get children to add faces of their own. They then challenge a partner to say what Fred is feeling. Alternatively, give children a word and get them to draw Fred in that mood. Play a game with a group. In turn each child imitates one of the faces. Can the others guess which one it is?

Welcome to our school

- Our school is a welcoming school because _____

_____

Things to think about

signs and notices
the school entrance
smiling people
seats and furniture
pictures
books

- Draw your school entrance.

Good things about my friend

- My friend is called

  _____

- Draw their picture here.

- Three good things about my friend are:

1. _____

   _____

2. _____

   _____

3. _____

   _____

Keeping safe in school

● What is dangerous about these pictures?

● Draw your own danger.

| run out of school | throw stones | play with doors |

Moving house

How does this family feel about moving house?

 Zak is _____ because he will have

a room of his own.

 Dad is _____ because the new

house will not need painting.

 Alice is _____ because she liked

her old bedroom.

 Mum is _____ because she might

not get on with the new neighbours.

 Kip is _____ because he doesn't

know what is happening.

 Baby is sleeping because she is

_____.

(sad)　(excited)　(pleased)　(tired)　(confused)　(worried)

Right ways and wrong ways

● Which is the right way ✓ ? Which is wrong ✗ ?

● What is the right way to do the things you ticked as wrong?

Permission

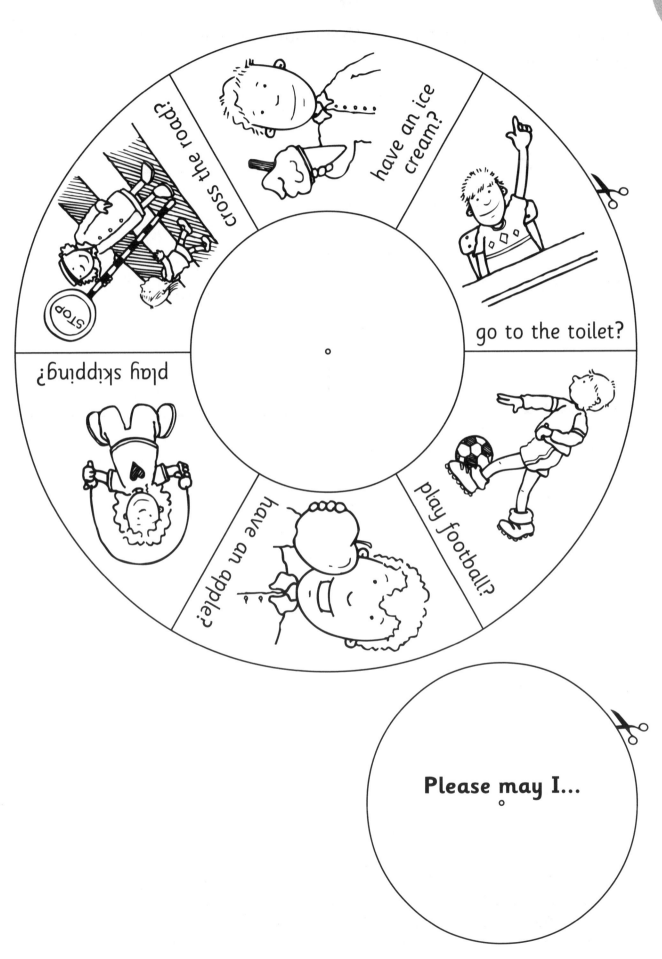

have an ice cream?

go to the toilet?

play football?

have an apple?

play skipping?

cross the road?

Please may I...

I am good at...

● Choose three stamps. Cut them out and stick them in the empty boxes.

I am good at _____.

I am good at _____.

I am good at _____.

● Draw your own picture here.

I am good at _____

football	writing	PE	reading

maths	tidying up	singing	making friends

Mistakes

Is it all right to...

 drop a cup?

Yes ☐ No ☐

 tread on a cat?

Yes ☐ No ☐

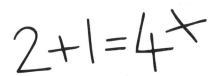 get a sum wrong?

Yes ☐ No ☐

 take the wrong hat?

Yes ☐ No ☐

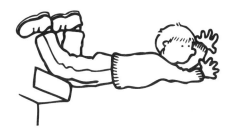 trip over the step?

Yes ☐ No ☐

 bump into the teacher?

Yes ☐ No ☐

Feelings

How is Fred feeling?

_____

_____

_____

Fred is feeling...

_____

_____

_____

angry	guilty	tired
thoughtful	happy	sad